The Gig Book

Showtunes

Published by
Wise Publications
14-15 Berners Street,
London W1T 3LJ, UK.

Exclusive Distributors:
Music Sales Limited
Distribution Centre,
Newmarket Road, Bury St Edmunds,
Suffolk IP33 3YB, UK.
Music Sales Pty Limited
20 Resolution Drive, Caringbah,
NSW 2229, Australia.

Order No. AM999691
ISBN 978-1-84938-436-0

This book © Copyright 2011
Wise Publications, a division of
Music Sales Limited.

Compiled by Nick Crispin.
Text by Graham Vickers.
Picture research by Jacqui Black.
Photographs courtesy of
Lebrecht Music & Arts.
Music engraved by Paul Ewers Music Design.
Edited by Adrian Hopkins.
Design by Fresh Lemon.

www.musicsales.com

Printed in Singapore.

Your Guarantee of Quality:
As publishers, we strive to produce every
book to the highest commercial standards.

The music has been freshly engraved and
the book has been carefully designed to
minimise awkward page turns and to make
playing from it a real pleasure.

Particular care has been given to specifying
acid-free, neutral-sized paper made from
pulps which have not been elemental chlorine
bleached.

This pulp is from farmed sustainable forests
and was produced with special regard for the
environment.

Throughout, the printing and binding
have been planned to ensure a sturdy,
attractive publication which should give
years of enjoyment.

If your copy fails to meet our high standards,
please inform us and we will gladly replace it.

Wise Publications
part of The Music Sales Group
London / New York / Paris / Sydney / Copenhagen / Berlin / Madrid / Hong Kong / Tokyo

The Gig Book Showtunes

Introduction

Musical theatre has a long history dating back to Antiquity, but in the 20th century the 'book musical' dominated and found its golden age on Broadway during the 1940s and 1950s. (The 'book musical' can be loosely defined as a musical play where songs and dancing are integrated with some serious dramatic purpose).

Great musicals were still being written and produced well into the 1960s, 1970s and beyond, but the classic model had its standards set in those twenty-odd years following World War II.

The breakthrough had come in the 1920s with *Show Boat*, a musical based on the 1926 novel by Edna Ferber. It was the first genuine American musical play — a drama with songs as opposed to a musical diversion with a thin storyline linking the songs. Written by Jerome Kern and Oscar Hammerstein II, its strong narrative was complemented by the songs, not interrupted by them. *Show Boat*'s unflinching story of life on the Mississippi steamer *Cotton Blossom* (featuring racial prejudice and doomed love) was a sensation both in New York and London. George and Ira Gershwin's 1935 'folk opera' *Porgy and Bess*, with its brave story of African-American life in South Carolina, continued the process but was clearly ahead of its time for Middle America. It took a few more years for another powerful musical play to appear and be widely accepted. Again Oscar Hammerstein II was involved, this time embarking on his successful professional partnership with Richard Rodgers. *Oklahoma!* (1943) was a vigorous story-driven musical and it was an immense success on both sides of the Atlantic. From then on a steady progression of great musicals would catch the world's imagination. *Carousel*. *South Pacific*. *Guys and Dolls*. *My Fair Lady*. *West Side Story*. *Cabaret*. *Chicago*. Almost without exception they drew on solid literary or dramatic sources. *Carousel* was adapted from Ferenc Molnár's play Liliom. *South Pacific* and *Guys and Dolls* were each based on a clutch of well-regarded short stories by James Michener and Damon Runyon respectively. *My Fair Lady* was a reworking of George Bernard Shaw's *Pygmalion*. And *West Side Story* perhaps aimed highest, looking to Shakespeare's *Romeo and Juliet* for inspiration. John Kander and Fred Ebb's *Cabaret* (1966) was based on Christopher Isherwood's *The Berlin Stories* and their *Chicago* (1975) had been well rehearsed as a 1926 play and two movies before it was turned into a bold and unflinching musical featuring murder, sexual exploitation and breath-taking cynicism.

In the 1960s the public mood had started to change, and, with the arrival of *Hair* in 1967, it was clear that other sorts of musicals — the 'rock' musical and the 'concept' musical— might gradually encroach on the territory of the traditional story-driven stage musical format. By the 1970s the 'jukebox' musical was also tentatively starting to emerge alongside more traditional offerings. *Ain't Misbehavin'* (songs of the Harlem Renaissance of the 20s and 30s) made its debut in the 1970s and *Leader Of The Pack* (the songs of Ellie Greenwich & Jeff Barry) premiered in the 1980s. Buddy: The Buddy Holly Story followed in the same decade, and by the late 1990s *Mamma Mia* would set the seal on the money-spinning format that made musicals out of popular song catalogues. Meanwhile London's West End, for years the grateful recipient of dynamic Broadway shows that usually outperformed flimsier home-grown fare, had begun to generate its own blockbuster musicals. Even so, in 1971 the British team of Andrew Lloyd Webber and Tim Rice launched *Jesus Christ Superstar* on Broadway before bringing it to London. Soon Lloyd Webber's *Evita*, *Cats* and *Phantom Of The Opera* would inject new life into the British musical, preparing the ground for other European offerings that would eventually also be welcomed on Broadway.

These days the musical can take a variety of forms, but the classics endure — witness the wealth of revivals to be seen on the London and Broadway stages and touring the world. *Hair*, *Oklahoma!*, *Chicago*, *Guys and Dolls*, *Cabaret*, *The Sound Of Music* and many more are regularly dusted off for new generations of audiences. Most are at least thirty years old and the granddaddy of them all, *Oklahoma!*, is now in its late sixties. This new collection puts a collection of the finest songs from most of these and other musicals in your hands and invites you to sing and play them for yourself. You may not end up on "The Great White Way", but you'll surely enjoy performing some of the vibrant and affecting songs that have gained a success on their own away from the stories they were written to serve… not to mention those pop hits given a new lease of life by their inclusion in a jukebox musical.

85
FAVOURITE
MUSICAL
SONGS

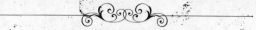

All Good Gifts

Words & Music by Stephen Schwartz

All good gifts a - round_____ us_____ are sent from

hea-ven a - bove._____Then thank the Lord, oh thank_ the Lord,

for all His love._____ 2. We

I real-ly wan-na thank you Lord._____

I want to thank you, Lord._ Thank you for all_ of your love._____ Oh,

thank you, Lord. I wan-na thank you, Lord;_____ thank you Lord.

As Long As He Needs Me

Words & Music by Lionel Bart

♩ = 84

As long as he needs me, oh yes he does need

me, in spite of what you see, I'm sure that he needs

me. Who else would love him still, when they've been used so

ill? He knows I al - ways will, as long as he needs

con moto

me. I miss him so much when he is gone. But when he's

poco rall.

near me, I don't let on. The way I

Aquarius

'This is the dawning of the age of Aquarius…' was the rallying cry of *Hair: The American Tribal Love-Rock Musical*. Back in 1967 when the show was first performed there was a sense that the hippie ethic could change society and, as a by-product, enable the mainstream musical theatre to feature mass nudity onstage to the delight of the radical young and the alarm of the conservative old. The show was the brainchild of Canadian musician and composer Galt MacDermot and the writing team of James Rado and Gerome Ragni. A world away from the traditional musical which usually based on some well-structured dramatic or literary source and crafted by professional teams like Rodgers & Hammerstein, *Hair* was in part a labour of love created by *arrivistes* who wanted to turn the revolutionary spirit of the 1960s into a piece of theatre. The plot was virtually non-existent to begin with although a move to Broadway's Biltmore Theater in April of 1968 resulted in some narrative tightening up, as did another production at London's Shaftesbury Avenue Theatre in September of the same year. Mainly though, *Hair* was about topical issues, not the niceties of traditional storytelling. Its concerns were conscription to the Vietnamese war, racial inequality, political repression, sexual freedom, lost innocence, drugs and long hair as an emblem of natural values. To say it was of its time is an understatement, but to dismiss it as naïve would be a mistake because *Hair* achieved what it set out to do. It became a pivotal event in the *Zeitgeist* of the 1960s. It invited the audience onstage as well as planting performers in the audience. In the true spirit of hippiedom it was at first more of a happening than a formal piece of musical theatre… yet it was both the first concept musical and the last stage musical to capture the public imagination on the scale that the old Broadway productions once did. Then there were the heartfelt songs. 'Aquarius' was the famous theme, but the show spawned several other hits, notably 'Good Morning Starshine' and 'Let The Sun Shine In', many of which are still quoted in contemporary movies and TV shows. *Hair* was revived in 2009/2010 on Broadway and in London's West End, a period piece to be viewed with nostalgia by those who knew it first time round, and perhaps met with puzzlement from younger audiences. As one reviewer noted, forty years on it was 'oddly poignant' to see the cast in its reinvented hippie finery 'racing downstage while delivering that tuneful salute to an age of Aquarius that still refuses to dawn'.

Aquarius

Words by James Rado & Gerome Ragni
Music by Galt MacDermot

Am

A - qua - ri - us.____

G   C   G

Har-mo-ny and un-der-stand - ing,   sym-pa-thy and trust   a -bound-

C   G   C

- ing.____   No more false-hoods or de - ri - sions,   gold - en

Am   G/B   C   E⁷/B   Am

liv - ing dreams of vi - sions._____

Mys - tic crys - tal re - ve -la - tion____

and the mind's_

Dm   Em   Dm

____ true li - be - ra - tion,_ A - qua - ri - us,____

Am

A - qua - ri - us.____

Be Italian

Words & Music by Maury Yeston

1. Be I - tal - ian, be I - tal - ian,
(2.) gen - tle, sen - ti - men - tal,

take a chance and try to steal a fier - y kiss. Be I-
go a - head and try to give my cheek a pat. But be

-tal - ian,___ be I - tal - ian, when you hold me, don't just
dar - ing,___ and un - car - ing, when you pinch me, try to

1.
hold me, but hold this! Ha, ha, ha, ha, ha, ha.

2.
2. Please___ be pinch me where there's fat! Ha! Be a

accel. poco a poco

sing - er,___ be a lov - er,___ pick the flow - er now be-

14

Beauty And The Beast

Music by Alan Menken
Words by Howard Ashman

Tale as old as time, tune as old as song.

Bit-ter-sweet and strange, find-ing you can change, learn-ing you were wrong.

Cer - tain as the sun ris - ing in the

east, tale as old as time, song as old as rhyme, Beau-ty and the

rall.

Beast. Tale as old as time, song as old as rhyme, Beau-ty and the

a tempo

Beast. *"Off to the cupboard with you now, Chip, it's past your bedtime. Goodnight love."*

17

Beggin'

Words & Music by Bob Gaudio & Peggy Farina

played_____ it hard and fast 'cause I had ev - 'ry - thing.
shad - ow of my life is hang - in' o - ver me.

Walked a - way,_____ warned me then,_____
Bro - ken man,_____ without a goal,_____

that ea - sy come and ea - sy go and it___ would end.___
don't e - ven stand a dev - il's chance to win___ my soul.___

(Beg - gin'.) I'm beg - gin'___ you,_____ won't you keep your

hand out, ba - by?___ (Beg - gin'.) Beg - gin',_____

___ put your lov - in' hand out, ba - by.
I need you to
I'm fight - ing hard to

19

un - der - stand___ that I tried so hard___ to
hold my own.___ No, I just can't___ make it

be a man.___ The kind of man you want
all a - lone.___ I'm hold - in' on, I

in the end,___ on - ly then can I___ be - gin to
can't go back,___ now that big brass___ ring___ is a

1.
live a - gain.___

2.
shade of black.___ (Beg - gin'.)

I'm beg - gin'___ you,___ won't you keep your hand out, ba - by?___

Repeat to fade

(Beg - gin'.) Beg - gin',___ put your lov - in' hand out, ba - by.

Bless Your Beautiful Hide

Words by John Mercer
Music by Gene De Paul

1. Bless your beau-ti-ful hide,___ wher-ev-er you may
2. Bless your beau-ti-ful hide,___ you're just as good as

be, we ain't met yet but I'm a-will-in' to bet
lost, I don't know your name but I'm a-stak-in' my claim

you're the gal___ for me.
lest your eyes___ is crossed.

Oh, I'd

swap my gun and I'd swap my mule, though who-ev-er took it would be

one big fool. Or pay your way through___

Pret - ty and trim and not too slim, hea - ven - ly eyes__ and

oh, that size. Sim - ple and sweet, but sas - sy as

can be.__ Bless her beau - ti - ful hide,__

__ yes, she's__ the girl__

for__ me.__

23

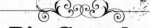

Big Spender

Words by Dorothy Fields
Music by Cy Coleman

Bring Him Home

Music by Claude-Michel Schönberg
Lyrics by Alain Boublil & Herbert Kretzmer

Can You Feel The Love Tonight

Words by Tim Rice
Music by Elton John

It's e-nough___ for this wide-eyed_ wan-der-er
that we got this far.___ And can you feel_ the love
___ to-night,___ how it's laid__ to rest?___
It's e-nough___ to make kings_ and___ va-ga-bonds_ be-
-lieve the ve - ry best.___

To Coda ⊕

2. There's a time__ for ev-'ry one, if they on - ly learn__

that the twist - ing ka - lei - do - scope moves us all__ in turn.__

There's a rhyme and rea - son to the wild__ out - doors,

D.S. al Coda

when the heart of this star-crossed voy-ag-er beats in time with yours. And

Coda

It's e - nough_____ to make kings__ and__ va - ga - bonds be-

molto rit.

- lieve the ve - ry best._____

30

Close Every Door

Music by Andrew Lloyd Webber
Lyrics by Tim Rice

la la la la la la, la la la la la la, la la la la la la la.) *(melody cue)*

la la la la la la, la la la la la la, la la la la la la la.) *(melody cue)*

D.S. al Coda

3. Just

⊕ **Coda**

world. 4. Close ev - 'ry door to me, keep those I

love from me chil - dren of Is - rael are nev - er a -

- lone. For we know we shall find our___ own peace of

rall.

mind, for we have been prom - ised, a land___ of our own.

33

Company

Words & Music by Stephen Sondheim

Phone rings, door chimes, in comes com-pa-ny!

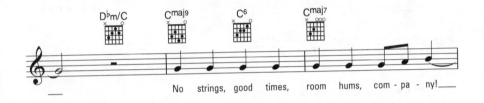

No strings, good times, room hums, com-pa-ny!

Late nights, quick bites, par-ty games,

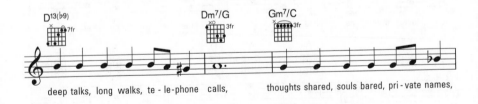

deep talks, long walks, te-le-phone calls, thoughts shared, souls bared, pri-vate names,

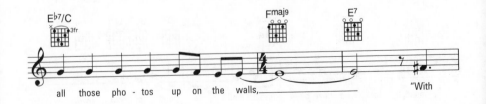

all those pho-tos up on the walls, "With

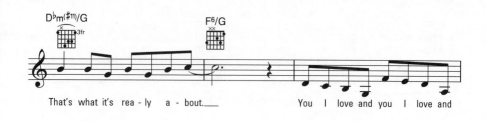

That's what it's rea - ly a - bout.___ You I love and you I love and

you and you I love and you I love and you I love and you and

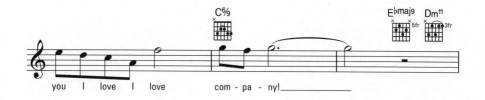

you I love I love com - pa - ny!___

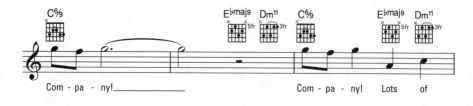

Com - pa - ny!___ Com - pa - ny! Lots of

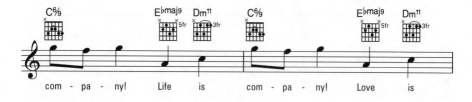

com - pa - ny! Life is com - pa - ny! Love is

Com - pa - ny!___ Com - pa - ny!___

Copacabana

Words & Music by Barry Manilow, Jack Feldman & Bruce Sussman

1. Her name was Lo - la,___ she was a show - girl___ with yel - low
(2.) Ri - co,___ he wore a dia - mond,___ he was es -

fea - thers in her hair___ and a dress___ cut down to there,___ she would me -
-cort - ed to his chair, he saw Lo - la danc - in' there.___ And when she

-ren - gue___ and do the cha - cha.___ And while she
fi - nished, he called her ov - er,___ but Ri - co

tried to be a star,___ To - ny al - ways tend - ed bar.___ A - cross a
went a bit too far,___ To - ny sailed a - cross the bar.___ And then the

crowd - ed___ floor, they worked from eight till___ four, they were
punch - es___ flew and chairs were smashed in___ two, there was

young and they had each oth - er, who could ask for more?
blood and a sin - gle gun shot, but just who shot who? At the

Co - pa,___ Co - pa - ca - ba - na,___ the

hot - test___ spot north of___ Ha - va - na.___ At the

Co - pa,___ Co - pa - ca - ba - na,___ mu - sic___ and pas - sion___ were

To Coda

al - ways the fash-ion. At the Co - pa___
(they fell in)
(she lost her)

1.

love. His name was

39

Dammit, Janet

A true phenomenon, Richard O'Brien's *Rocky Horror Show* went beyond being a cult musical to ingrain itself permanently into pop culture. It was triggered by an idea from O'Brien (already the veteran of a UK touring production of *Hair*) developed when he abruptly left a production of *Jesus Christ Superstar*, allegedly after refusing to tap dance in his role of Herod. With time on his hands, he started writing some songs for an untitled rock musical. Later, working with Superstar director Jim Sharman on another project at London's Royal Court Theatre he started to flesh out the idea. Sharman put together a creative team that included Richard Hartley as musical director and *The Rocky Horror Show* was born. It was originally performed upstairs at The Royal Court, then it camped out (in every sense) in a couple of nearby Chelsea buildings due for demolition. The plot defies summary other than to say that it concerns strait-laced middle-American young

couple Brad Majors and Janet Weiss who are forced by a flat tyre and a rainstorm to seek a telephone in the sort of forbidding castle only found in horror films. Inside they discover transgender sex, body-building, and a Frankenstein-style laboratory complete with its triumphant product: a man-made man, Rocky Horror. Extravagance, excess and implausibility are not flaws but essential ingredients of the plot. Processed by O'Brien's high-camp imagination they coalesce into a musical show so appealingly outrageous that it has prompted generations of fans to dress up as characters. A 1975 movie fixed the show in time and has itself become a cult. O'Brien remains associated with Rocky Horror and its perennial touring versions, as well as appearing on TV, often trading on the creepy image generated by the character he played in his own creation, the weird servant Riff Raff. Of the show's songs, 'Dammit, Janet' lays some claim to being the most famous, its title having now passed into the English language as one of those interjections that is at the same time both meaningless and a signifier of familiarity with *The Rocky Horror Show*. The song marks Brad's early awkward bid to declare his love and features various excruciating attempts to find rhymes for his girlfriend's prosaic first name, ending with: 'Dammit, Janet, I love you...'

Dammit, Janet

Words & Music by Richard O'Brien

41

Here's a ring to prove that I'm_ no jok-er._

There's three ways that love_ can grow_ that's good,

bad or me-di-o-cre._ Oh J. A. N. E. T. I love you

so. *(Janet)* 3.Oh it's nic-er than Bet - ty Mun - ro had, (Oh Brad)
(Verse 4 see block lyrics)

now we're en - gaged and I'm so glad, (oh Brad) that you met mum and you know_

_ dad, (Oh Brad) I've one thing to say_ and that's Brad, I'm mad for you too._

42

Verse 2:
The road was long but I ran it (Janet)
There's a fire in my heart and you fan it (Janet)
If there's one fool for you then I am it (Janet)
I've something to say and that's
Damn it, Janet, I love you.

Verse 4:
And that's go see the man who began it (Janet)
When we met in his science exam, it (Janet)
Made me give you the eye and then panic (Janet)
Now I've one thing to say and that's
Damn it, Janet, I love you.

Dancing Queen

Words & Music by Benny Andersson, Stig Anderson & Björn Ulvaeus

44

looking out for a place to go, mm,

where they play the right music, getting in the swing you come to

look for a King.

2. Anybody could be that guy,
3. You're a teaser, you turn 'em on,

night is young and the music's high,
leave 'em burning and then you're gone,

with a bit of rock music ev'rything is fine,
looking out for another anyone will do,

you're in the

mood for a dance.___ And when you get the___ chance_____

___ you are___ the danc - ing___ queen, young and___ sweet, on - ly

se - ven - teen,___ danc - ing___ queen,

feel the___ beat___ from the tam - bour - ine,_____

To Coda ⊕

you can dance,___ you can jive,_____

hav - ing___ the time of___ your life,___ oh,_____ see that___ girl___

watch that_ scene, dig-gin' the dan-cing_ queen._

D.S. al Coda

Coda

hav-ing_ the time of_ your life,_ oh,_ see that_ girl,_

watch that_ scene,_ dig-gin' the dan-cing_ queen._

Dig-gin' the

Repeat to fade

dan-cing_ queen._

47

Defying Gravity

Words & Music by Stephen Schwartz

1. Some-thing has changed with-in me, some-thing is___ not the same.
2. I'm through ac-cept-ing lim-its 'cause some-one says they're so.

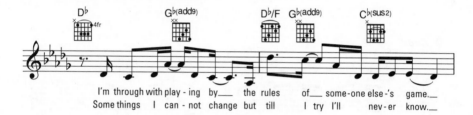

I'm through with play-ing by___ the rules of___ some-one else-'s game.___
Some things I can-not change but till I try I'll nev-er know.___

Too late for___ se-cond guess-ing, too late___ to go back to sleep.
Too long I've been a-fraid of los-ing love___ I guess I've lost.

It's time to trust my in-stincts, close my eyes and leap. It's time___ to
Well, if that's love it comes at much too high a cost. I'd soon-er

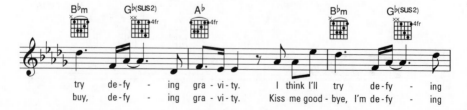

try de-fy - ing gra-vi-ty. I think I'll try de-fy - ing
buy, de-fy - ing gra-vi-ty. Kiss me good-bye, I'm de-fy - ing

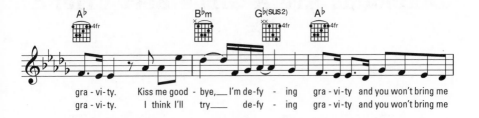

gra - vi - ty.   Kiss me good - bye,___ I'm de-fy - ing   gra - vi-ty and you won't bring me
gra - vi - ty.   I think I'll   try___   de-fy - ing   gra - vi-ty and you won't bring me

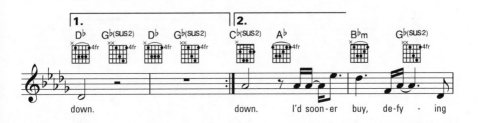

down.   down.   I'd soon-er buy, de-fy - ing

gra - vi - ty.   Kiss me good - bye,___ I'm de-fy - ing   gra - vi - ty.   I think I'll

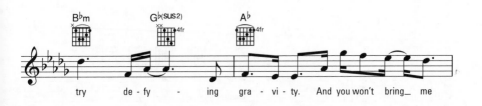

try   de-fy - ing   gra - vi - ty.   And you won't   bring___ me

down.   Bring me   down.   Oh!_____

Diamonds Are A Girl's Best Friend

Words by Leo Robin
Music by Jule Styne

Original key: D♭ major

♩ = 110

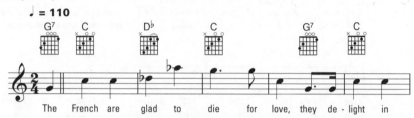

The French are glad to die for love, they de-light in

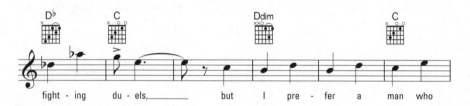

fight-ing du-els,_____ but I pre-fer a man who

poco rall.　　　　　　　　　　**a tempo**

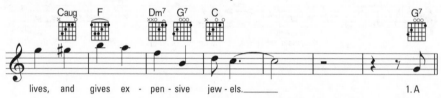

lives, and gives ex-pen-sive jew-els._____　　　1. A

kiss on the hand may be quite Con-ti-nen-tal but dia-monds are a
(2.) may come a time when a lass needs a law-yer, but dia-monds are a
(Verse 3 see block lyrics)

girl's best friend,_____ a kiss may be grand but it
girl's best friend,_____ there may come a time when a

won't pay the ren-tal on your hum-ble flat_____ or help you at the
hard boiled em-ploy-er thinks you're aw-ful nice,___ but get that "ice" or

Au-to-mat. Men grow cold as girls grow old and we
else no dice. He's your guy when stocks are high, but be -

all lose our charms in the end._____ But square cut or
-ware when they start to de - scend._____ It's then that those

pear-shape, these rocks don't lose their shape, dia-monds are a girl's best
lous-es go back to their spous-es, dia-monds are a girl's best

1, 2.

3.

friend._____ 2. There friend._____
friend._____ 3. Ro -

Verse 3:
Romance is divine, and I'm not one to knock it
But diamonds are a girl's best friend
Romance is divine, yeah, but where can you hock it
When the flame is gone, you just try and pawn a tired Don Juan
Time rolls on, and youth is gone and you can't straighten up when you bend
But stiff-back or stiff-knees, you stand straight at Tiffany's
Diamonds are a girl's best friend.

Don't Cry For Me Argentina

Music by Andrew Lloyd Webber
Lyrics by Tim Rice

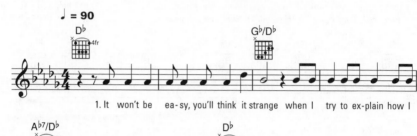

1. It won't be ea-sy, you'll think it strange when I try to ex-plain how I

feel, that I still need your love af-ter all that I've done:____ You won't be -

- lieve me, all you will see is a girl you once knew, al-though she's dressed up to the

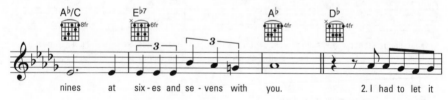

nines at six-es and se-vens with you. 2. I had to let it

hap-pen, I had to change; could-n't stay all my life down at heel, look-ing

out of the win-dow, stay-ing out of the sun. So I chose

Slow Tango feel

free - dom,　run - ning a - round try - ing ev - ry - thing new;　but

no - thing im - pressed me　at　all,　I　nev - er ex - pect - ed　it　to.

Don't cry for me Ar - gen - ti - na,＿＿＿ the truth is I nev - er

left you, all through my wild days, my mad ex - ist - ence, I kept my

pro - mise, Don't keep your dis - tance.＿ 3. And as for

for - tune and as for fame. I nev - er in - vi - ted them

in, though it seemed to the world they were all I de - sired. They are il -

53

-lu - sions, they're not the so-lu - tions they pro-mised to be, the

ans - wer was here all the time_____ I

poco rall.

love you and hope you love me.

Slower

Don't cry for me Ar - gen - ti - na. Mm_____

(bouche fermè)

Tempo I

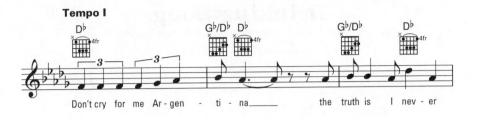

Don't cry for me Ar - gen - ti - na____ the truth is I nev - er

left you, all through my wild days my mad ex -

- ist - ence, I kept my pro - mise, don't keep your dis - tance.

Have I said too much? There's no - thing more I can think of to

say to you. But all you have to do is

look at me to know that ev - 'ry word is true.

55

Drinking Song

Words & Music by Sigmund Romberg & Dorothy Donnelly

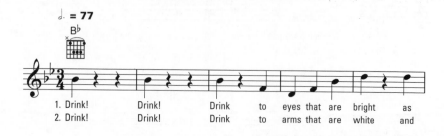

1. Drink! Drink! Drink to eyes that are bright as
2. Drink! Drink! Drink to arms that are white and

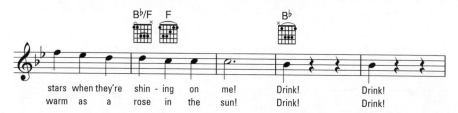

stars when they're shin - ing on me! Drink! Drink!
warm as a rose in the sun! Drink! Drink!

Drink to lips that are red and sweet as the fruit on the
Drink to hearts that will love one, on - ly when I am the

tree! Here's a hope that those bright eyes will
one! Here's a hope that those soft arms will

shine lov - ing - ly, long - ing - ly soon in - to mine!
twine ten - der - ly, trust - ing - ly soon a - round mine!

Electricity

Words by Lee Hall
Music by Elton John

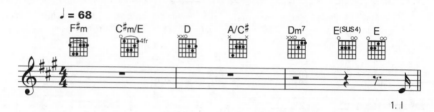

can't real - ly ex - plain it,   I   have - n't got the words.___   It's a
(2, 3) bit like be - ing an - gry, it's   a   bit like be - ing scared,__   con-

feel - ing   that   you   can't   con - trol.____   I   sup -
-fused and   all mixed up and mad as   hell.____   It's

-pose it's   like for - get - ting,   los - ing who you are___   and at the
like when you've been cry - ing and you're emp - ty and you're full.___   I

same   time___   some - thing makes you   whole.   It's
don't know what it is,   it's hard to   tell.

58

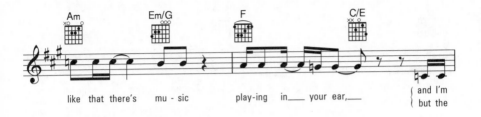

like that there's mu-sic play-ing in___ your ear,___ { and I'm
{ but the

list-'ning and I'm list-'ning and then I dis-ap-pear.___ And then I
mu-sic is im-pos-si-ble, im-pos-si-ble to hear.___ But then I

feel a change like a fire___ deep in-side.___)
feel it move me like a burn-ing deep in-side.___)

Some-thing burst-ing me wide o-pen, im-pos-si-ble___ to hide.___ And

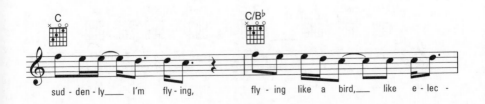

sud-den-ly___ I'm fly-ing, fly-ing like a bird,___ like e-lec-

-tri - ci - ty.   E - lec - tri - ci - ty,   sparks in -

-side   of   me.___   And I'm free,   I'm

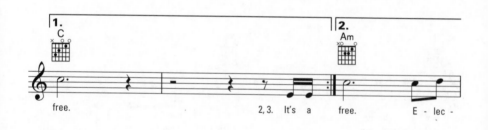

free.   2, 3. It's a   free.   E - lec -

-tri - ci - ty.   Sparks in - side of me___   and I'm free,   I'm (It's a...)

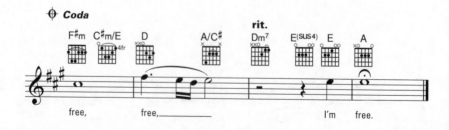

free,   free,_____   I'm free.

Five Guys Named Moe

Words & Music by Larry Wynn & Jerry Bresler

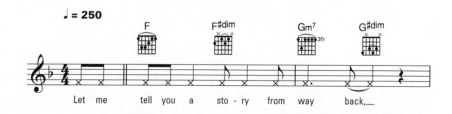

Let me tell you a sto-ry from way back,__

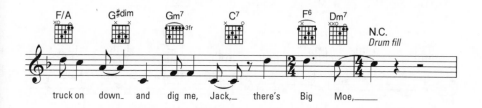

truck on down_ and dig me, Jack,__ there's Big Moe,__

Lit-tle Bid-dy Moe,

Four-Eyed_ Moe,____ No Moe,

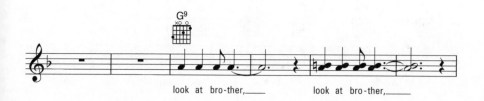

look at bro-ther,____ look at bro-ther,____

look   at   bro - ther,   Eat   Moe.____

N.C.

Moe,   Moe,   Moe,   Moe,   Moe._____

Who's the great-est band a - round,   makes the cats jump   up and   down,

who's the talk   of   rhy-thm   town,   five   guys named   Moe, that's   us!

When they start to   beat it   out,__   ev-'ry-bo-dy   jumps__ and   shouts,

tell me who the cri-tics all   rave a - bout,__   five   guys named Moe.   Ah,

we came out of no - where, that don't mean a thing,____

we rate high, you'll know why_ when you hear us sing,____

sing, sing, sing, sing.____

High brow, low brow,_ they all a - gree,

we're the best in har - mo - ny,____ I'm

tell-ing you folks, you real - ly ought to see five guys named Moe.

We came out of no - where, that don't mean a thing,

we rate high,_ you'll know why_ when you hear us

sing._

We're the great - est band a - round, make the cats jump

up and down,_ we're the talk of

rhy - thm town,_ five guys named Moe. Not

Everyday

Words & Music by Charles Hardin & Norman Petty

Original key: E♭ major

1. Ev - 'ry day it's a - get - tin' clos - er,
2. Ev - 'ry day it's a - get - tin' fast - er,

go - ing fast - er than a roll - er - coast - er.
ev - 'ry - one said "Go a - head and ask her."

Love like yours will tru - ly come my

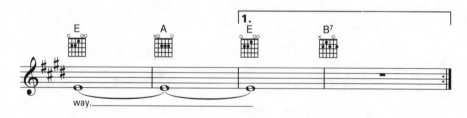

1.

way.

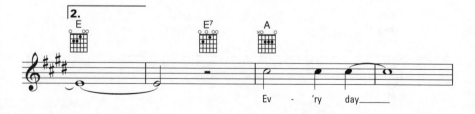

2.

Ev - 'ry day

seems a lit - tle long - er. Ev - 'ry way___

love's a lit - tle strong - er. Come what may, do you ev - er

long for true love from me?___

3. Ev - 'ry day it's a - get - tin' clos - er, go - ing

fast - er than a roll - er - coast - er. Love like yours will

tru - ly come my way.___

Feeling Good

Words & Music by Leslie Bricusse & Anthony Newley

Verse 2:
Fish in the sea, you know how I feel
River running free, you know how I feel
Blossom on the tree, you know how I feel
It's a new dawn, it's a new day
It's a new life for me, feeling good.

Getting To Know You

Words by Oscar Hammerstein II
Music by Richard Rodgers

1. Get-ting to know you, get-ting to know all a - bout you.
(2.) know you, get-ting to feel free and ea - sy.

Get-ting to like you, get-ting to hope you like
When I am with you, get-ting to know what to

me. Get-ting to know you,
say. Have-n't you

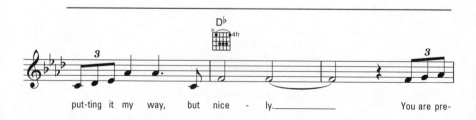

put-ting it my way, but nice - ly. You are pre-

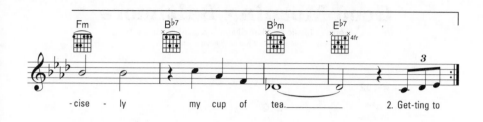

-cise - ly   my cup of tea._____   2. Get-ting to

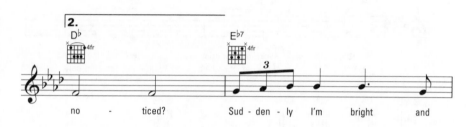

2.

no - ticed?   Sud-den-ly I'm   bright   and

bree - zy.   Be - cause of   all   the

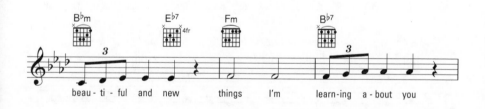

beau - ti - ful and new   things   I'm   learn-ing a - bout you

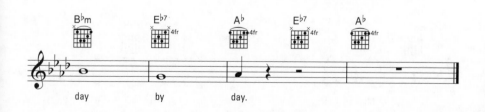

day   by   day.

Good Morning Baltimore

Words & Music by Marc Shaiman & Scott Wittman

♩ = 132

1. Oh, oh, oh. Woke up to-day feel-ing the way I
2. Oh, oh, oh. Look at my hair. What "do" can com-pare with

al - ways do. Oh, oh, oh. Hun-gry for some-thing that
mine to - day? Oh, oh, oh. I've got my hair-spray and

I can't eat, then I hear the beat. That rhy-thm of town starts
ra - di - o, I'm read-y to go. The rats on the streets all

call - ing me down. It's like a mes-sage from high a - bove
dance 'round my feet. They seem to say, "Tra - cy, it's up to you."

Oh, oh, oh. Pull - ing me out to the
So, oh, oh. Don't hold me back, 'cause to -

smiles and the streets that I love. Good morn - ing,
-day all my dreams will come true. Good morn - ing,

Bal - ti - more!   Ev - 'ry day's like an o - pen door,
Bal - ti - more!   There's the flash - er who lives next door.

ev - ry night is a fan - ta - sy,   ev - 'ry sound's like a
There's the bum on his bar - room stool.   They wish me luck on my

sym - pho - ny. }
way to school. }   Good morn - ing, Bal - ti - more!

And some day when I take to the floor, the world's gon-na wake up and_ see

1.

Bal - ti - more and   me.

73

2.

E♭

me.   I

C♭   G♭/B♭   A♭m7

know ev-'ry step.   I know ev-'ry song.   I know there's a place where

A♭m/B♭ G♭/B♭   D♭   A♭/C

I   be-long.   I   see all those par-ty lights shin-ing a-head.   So

B♭m7   A♭/C   B♭(SUS4)   B♭

some-one in-vite me be-fore I   drop dead!____

E♭   E♭/G   A♭

3. So,   oh,   oh. Give me a chance, 'cause when I start to dance I'm a

Cm/B♭ B♭   A♭   E♭   E♭/G

mo - vie___ star.___   Oh,   oh,   oh. Some-thing in-side of me

74

makes me move when I hear the groove. My ma tells me, "No," ___ but my

feet tell me, "Go." It's like a drum-mer in - side my heart.___

Oh, oh, oh. Don't make me wait one more

mo - ment for my life to start.___

___ I love you,

Bal - ti - more! Ev - 'ry day's like an o - pen ___ door, ___

ev-'ry night is a fan-ta-sy, ev-'ry sound's like a

sym - pho - ny. And I pro - mise, Bal - ti - more,

that some day when I take to the floor, the world's gon-na wake up____ and____

see, gon - na wake up and see_____

Bal - ti - more and me. Bal - ti - more____ and____

me, Bal - ti - more and____ me!____

76

Happy Talk

South Pacific is among the best of the golden age Broadway musicals. Richard Rodgers & Oscar Hammerstein II had already enjoyed enormous success with *Oklahoma!* and *Carousel* when their *South Pacific* premiered at the Shubert Theatre in New Haven, Connecticut in early 1949. After the try-out it went to Broadway the same year to enormous acclaim. With its bracing story mix of military conflict in the Pacific, miscegenation and good old American optimism, it owed its plot to three James Michener stories from his prize winning collection 'Tales of the South Pacific'. Producer Josh Logan helped with the show's book because Hammerstein (the son of German- and British-born parents) could not render heroine Nelly Forbush's southern speech patterns plausibly. Logan, like Michener, was a war veteran and supported the authors in retaining one of the grittier

elements of the show, notably their song (highly controversial for 1949) about the roots of racial prejudice 'You've Got To Be Carefully Taught'. The show's major hit songs were generally rather more romantic or upbeat — 'Some Enchanted Evening', 'Younger Than Springtime', 'There Is Nothing Like A Dame' — but rather ironically 'Happy Talk', which charmed audiences in the 1950s, was later sometimes dropped from productions on the grounds of political correctness. The show that originally had the courage to include 'You've Got To Be Carefully Taught' was now criticised for the faux-pidgin English aspect of its 'Happy Talk' scene in which a Polynesian souvenir dealer seeks to set up her daughter with an American lieutenant. Many of the show's songs have been covered over the past 60 years although the once-innocent 'Happy Talk', being rather dependent on its context in the show, was only occasionally attempted. That didn't stop The Damned's Raymond Burns covering it and reaching No. 1 in 1982 in his solo guise of Captain Sensible.

Happy Talk

Words by Oscar Hammerstein II
Music by Richard Rodgers

Hap - py talk, keep talk - in' hap-py talk.

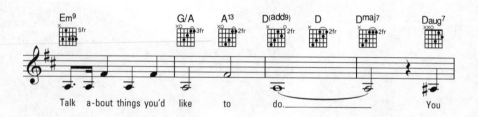

Talk a-bout things you'd like to do. _____ You

got to have a dream; _____ if you don't have a dream, ___

how you gon - na have a dream come true? _____

1. Talk a - bout a moon
2. Talk a - bout the star

float - in' in the sky, look - in' like a li - ly on a lake.

look - in' like a toy, peek - in' through the branch - es of a tree.

Talk a - bout a bird learn - in' how to fly,

Talk a - bout the girl, talk a - bout the boy,

mak - in' all the mus - ic he can make.

count - in' all the rip - ples on the sea.

Hap - py

talk, keep talk - in' hap - py talk.

Talk a - bout things you'd

like to do.

You got to have a dream; if

you don't have a dream, how you gon - na have a dream come

79

true?

Talk a-bout the boy, say-in' to the girl "Gol-ly, baby, I'm a luck-y cuss!" Talk a-bout the girl say-in' to the

80

Grow For Me

Words by Howard Ashman
Music by Alan Menken

no - thing__ but heart-ache and hurt. I'm beg-ging you
po - tash,__ you've giv-en me zip! Oh God, how I

sweet - ly,___ I'm down on my knees:_____ oh
mist you!__ Oh pod, how you tease!_____ Now

1.
please,_____ grow__ for me!_____ 2. I've giv-en you

2.
please,_____ grow__ for me! I've giv-en you

south-ern__ ex-po-sure__ to get you to thrive. I've pinched you back

hard, like__ I'm s'posed ta:__ you're bare-ly a-live. I've tried you at

83

lev - els___ of mois - ture___ from de - sert___ to mud; and I've

giv - en you grow - lights and min - er - al sup - ple - ments.

What do you want from me? Blood? Ouch!

Damn roses! Damn thorns! Clumsy me! Look what I did, Two-ey!

Hey, you're opening up! What made you do that?

I think I know what made you do that. Well, I guess a few drops couldn't hurt.

84

As long as you don't make a habit out of it, or anything.

I've giv - en you sun - light,__ I've giv - en you rain; looks like you're not hap - py__ 'less I op - en a vein! I'll give you a

rit.

few drops,__ if that - 'll ap - pease.__ Now

molto rit.

please,__ oh, oh, oh please,__ grow for me!

a tempo

molto rall.

85

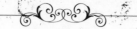

Honeysuckle Rose

Words by Andy Razaf
Music by Fats Waller

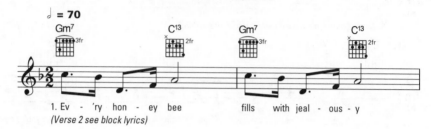

1. Ev - 'ry hon - ey bee   fills   with jeal - ous - y
(Verse 2 see block lyrics)

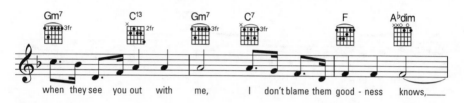

when they see you out with   me,   I don't blame them good - ness   knows,____

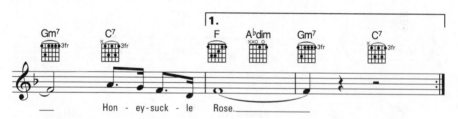

1.

____ Hon - ey - suck - le   Rose.____

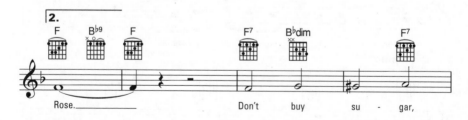

2.

Rose.____   Don't   buy   su - gar,

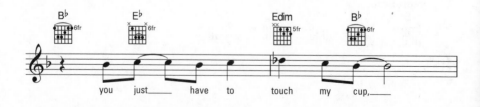

you just____ have to   touch   my   cup,____

you're my sug - ar, it's sweet_ when you

stir it up.___ 3. When I'm tak - ing sips, from your tas - ty lips,

seems the ho - ney fair - ly drips, you're con-fec - tion good - ness knows,___

___ Hon - ey - suck - le Rose.___

Verse 2:
When you're passin' by
Flowers droop and sigh
And I know the reason why
You're much sweeter goodness knows
Honeysuckle Rose.

How To Succeed In Business Without Really Trying

Words & Music by Frank Loesser

How to ob-serve per-son-nel, how to se-lect whom to lunch with, how to a-void pet-ty friends, how to be-gin mak-ing con-tacts. How to walk in-to a con-fe-rence room____ with an i- -dea, bril-liant bus-'ness i-dea, that-'ll make your ex-pense ac-count zoo-oom.____ This book is all that I need, How to, how to suc-ceed.____

How Many Tears?

Music by Claude-Michel Schönberg
Lyrics by Alain Boublil & Stephen Clark

Verse 2:
How many tears through the years can I cry?
How many tears until my heart runs dry
Through the fights that a woman must fight
Only to do what she feels must be right.

I Dreamed A Dream

Music by Claude-Michel Schönberg
Original Lyrics by Alain Boublil & Jean-Marc Natel
English Lyrics by Herbert Kretzmer

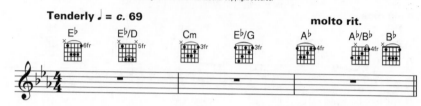

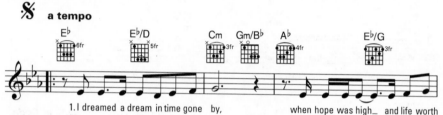

1. I dreamed a dream in time gone by, when hope was high and life worth

(Verses 2 & 3 see block lyrics)

liv - ing. I dreamed that love would nev - er die,

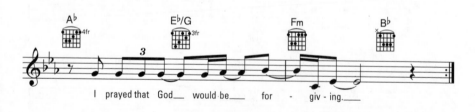

I prayed that God would be for - giv - ing.

But the ti - gers come at night, with their voi - ces soft as

thun-der,___ as they tear__ your hopes a - part,___

and they turn your dream to shame.___

Coda

But he was gone when au-tumn came.

Broadly

4. And still I dreamed he'd come to me,

that we will live___ the years__ to - geth - er;___

but there are dreams__ that can - not be,___

93

and there are storms we can-not wea - ther.

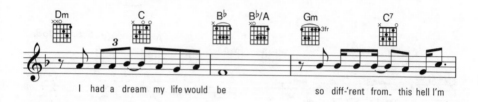

I had a dream my life would be   so diff-'rent from_ this hell I'm

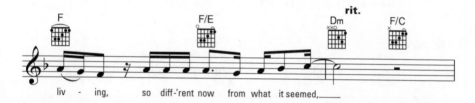

rit.

liv - ing,   so diff-'rent now from what it seemed,____

Slower

now life has killed_ the dream   I dreamed.

rit. poco a poco

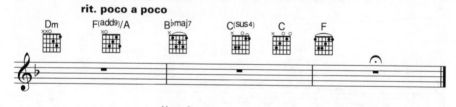

Verse 2:
Then I was young and unafraid
And dreams were made and used and wasted
There was no ransom to be paid
No song unsung, no wine untasted.

Verse 3:
He slept a summer by my side
He filled my days with endless wonder
He took my childhood in his stride
But he was gone when autumn came.

I Still Believe

Firmly in the tradition of taking an existing piece and reworking it into a popular musical, *Miss Saigon* came from the same team that wrote *Les Misérables*, Claude-Michel Schönberg and Alain Boublil. This time the source was Puccini's opera *Madame Butterfly*, a story of the doomed love between an American naval lieutenant and a young geisha in Japan at the start of the 20th century. *Miss Saigon* transfers the action to Vietnam in the 1970s and a romance between an American G.I. and a Vietnamese bar girl on the eve of the American military withdrawal from the country. It opened in London's Theatre Royal in 1989 and ran at the same venue for a decade. It enjoyed another 10-year run in New York at The Broadway Theater from 1991 to 2001. Many of the songs were

primarily in service of the plot and *Miss Saigon*, despite its enduring popularity, does not belong to the era when a successful musical spawned half a dozen or more major hits and so embedded itself in the popular music of the age. Even so 'I Still Believe' is an affecting song of longing and optimism that is sung by Kim the bar girl towards the end of Act 1. The role made the international career of the Filipina Lea Salonga who, at the age of 18 was already a veteran performer of ten years' experience having appeared in Philippine productions of *The King and I*, *Annie* and *Fiddler on the Roof* as well as a slew of Tennessee Williams dramas. She would go on to star in the Broadway version of *Miss Saigon* too, despite being caught up in a hysterical flurry of objections from the US Actors Equity Association which objected to a Filipina being imported almost as much as it objected to Welsh actor Jonathan Pryce playing the Asian character of The Engineer in prosthetic makeup; this was seen as a slight to under-employed Asian actors in America. In fact his character was Eurasian and Pryce complained at the time that this sort of doctrinaire thinking might lead to his only ever being able to play Welshmen. Both were allowed to perform in the end. Meanwhile after two megahits Schönberg and Boublil have yet to hit the same heights with any of the three shows that followed Miss Saigon, musicals based respectively on the legends of French imposter Martin Guerre, Irish pirate queen Gráinne O'Malley and Dumas' tragic heroine Marguerite Gautier, *La Dame aux Camélias* whose plight had already been musicalised in Verdi's *La Traviata*.

PLAYBILL
THE BROADWAY THEATRE

M⚹SS Saigon

I Still Believe

Music by Claude-Michel Schönberg
Lyrics by Alain Boublil & Richard Maltby Jr.
Adapted from original French Lyrics by Alain Boublil

Freely (♩ = 100)

(Kim) 1. Last night I watched him sleep-ing, my bo - dy pressed
(Ellen) 2. Last night I watched you sleep-ing, once more the night - mare

to him.
came.
And then he start - ed speak - ing,
I heard you cry out some - thing;
the
a

name I heard him speak
word that sound - ed like_____
was Kim.
a name.
Yes I
And it

know that this was years a - go,
hurts me more than I can bear,
but when moon-light fills my room
know-ing part of you I'll_____
I
ne - ver

know you are here still.
share, ne - ver know._____
I
But

96

still,_____ I still_____ be - lieve you
still,_____ I still_____ be - lieve the

will_____ re - turn, I____ know you will. My
time_____ will come when no - thing keeps us a - part. My

1.

heart,_____ a - gainst all odds holds still, yes,
heart,_____ for - e - ver

still,_____ I still_____ be - lieve. I____

know_____ as long as I can keep be - liev - ing,_____ I'll

live, I'll live,_____ love can - not die,

97

I Will Survive

Words & Music by Dino Fekaris & Freddie Perren

Freely

At first I was a-fraid, I was pet-ri-fied,___ kept think-ing I could ne-ver live___ with-out you

by my side, but then I spent so ma-ny nights think-ing how you did me wrong and I grew

strong and I learned how to get a-long.___ 1. And so you're back from out-er space___
(Verse 3 see block lyrics)

___ I just walked in to find_ you here_ with that_ sad look up-on_ your face. I should have changed_

___ that stu-pid lock,_ I should have made___ you leave your key___ if I'd-'ve known___

for just_ one sec - ond you'd be back to both - er me._ Go on now

go! Walk out the door.__ Just turn a-round____ now 'cause you're not

wel-come an - y - more. Weren't you the one_ who tried to hurt_

_ me with good-bye?_ Did you think I'd crum - ble?__ Did you think I'd

lay down_ and die? Oh no, not I, I will sur - vive.__ Oh,_ as

long as I know how to love_ I know I'll stay a-live. I've got all my life to live,_ and I've got

all my love to give_and I'll sur-vive.__ I will sur-vive.__ Hey, hey._

101

all the strength_ I had__ not to fall a - part,_____ kept try - ing

hard to mend the piec - es of my bro - ken heart, and I spent oh so ma - ny nights just feel - ing

sor - ry for my - self,_ I used to cry___ but now I hold my head up high. 3. And you see

Coda

Oh! Go on__ now

Verse 3:
And you see me somebody new
I'm not that chained up little person
Still in love with you
And so you feel like dropping in
And just expect me to be free
Well, now I'm saving all my loving
For someone who's loving me.

If I Were A Rich Man

Words by Sheldon Harnick
Music by Jerry Bock

103

town;   a   fine tin roof with   real wood-en floors   be-low.

There could be   one long stair-case   just go-ing up and   one ev-en long-er com-ing

rall.

down;   and   one more lead-ing   no-where just for   show.

I'd fill my yard with chicks and   tur-keys and geese and ducks for the town to see and

hear;   squawk-ing   just   as   nois - i - ly   as   they   can.

And each loud quack and cluck and   gob - ble and honk will   land like a trum-pet on the
(*imitate sounds*)

rall.

D.C. al Coda

ear;   as   if   to say here   lives   a   wealth-y   man._____ (*Sigh*)

104

man. I see my wife, my Gold - e, look - ing like a rich man's

wife with a pro - per dou - ble chin; su - per - vis - ing meals to her heart's de-

- light. I see her put - ting on airs and strut - ting like a pea - cock

Oy! What a hap - py mood she's in. Scream - ing at the ser - vants day and

night. The most im - port - ant men in town will come to fawn on___me;

they will ask me to ad - vise them.___ Like So - lo - mon the wise, "If you

please, Reb Tev - ye, par - don me, Reb Tev - ye."

105

Pos - ing prob - lems that would cross a rab - bi's eyes.

Freely

Boi, boi, boi, boi, boi, boi, boi, boi, boi.____

Deliberately (in tempo)

Fm⁷ B♭⁷ E♭maj⁷ B♭m⁶ C⁷

And it won't make one bit of dif - f'rence if I ans - wer right or wrong?

Fm F♯dim G⁷ **rall.** C⁷

When you're rich, they think you real - ly know. If I were

Reflective, lyrical, soft

F G⁷ C A⁷

rich, I'd have the time that I lack, to sit in the syn - a - gogue and pray; and

Dm⁷ G⁷ C C⁷

may - be have a seat by the east - ern wall. And I'd dis -

Fm B♭⁷ E♭maj⁷ B♭m⁶ C⁷

- cuss the ho - ly books with the learn - ed men sev - en ho - urs ev - 'ry day;

106

that would be the sweet-est thing of all._____ (*Sigh*)

If I were a rich man, dai- dle, dee dle, dai- dle, dig- guh, dig- guh, dee dle, dai- dle, dum.

All day long I'd bid- dy, bid-dy bum. If I were a weath-ly man, I

would- n't have to work hard, dai- dle, dee- dle, dai- dle, dig- guh, dig- guh, dee- dle, dai- dle,

dum. Lord, who made the li- on and the lamb, you de - creed I

should be what I am; would it spoil some vast e - ter- nal plan,

if I were a wealth- y man?_____

If He Really Knew Me

Words by Carole Bayer Sager
Music by Marvin Hamlisch

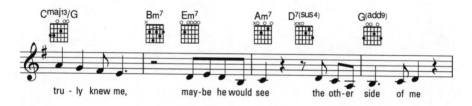

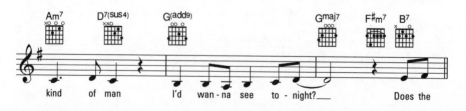

who_____ I am. am._____

(Vernon) If there were no mu - sic, if my___ me - lo - dies___

___ stopped play - ing, would I be the kind of man___

she'd wan-na see to - night?___ What the hell, it's just a

din - ner and if this does-n't work, that's it and can I___

real - ly be___ so hun - gry   for a   hit.

If   she real - ly   knew   me,

if   she'd take the   time   to   un - der-stand,

may - be she could find   me,   the part   I

left be-hind me,   may-be she'd re - mind   me_____   of

who   I   am._____

111

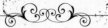

If I Loved You

Words by Oscar Hammerstein II
Music by Richard Rodgers

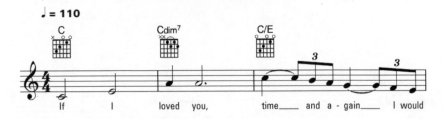

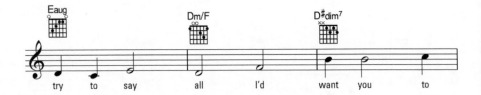

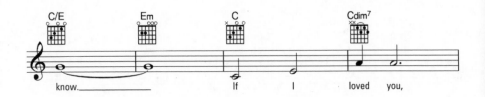

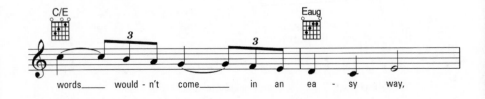

It Might As Well Be Spring

Words by Oscar Hammerstein II
Music by Richard Rodgers

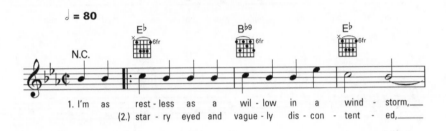

1. I'm as rest-less as a wil-low in a wind-storm,
(2.) star-ry eyed and vague-ly dis-con-tent-ed,

I'm as jump-y as a pup-pet on a string.
like a night-in-gale with-out a song to sing.

I'd say that I had Spring Fev-er,
Oh, why should I have Spring Fev-er,

but I know it is-n't
when it is-n't ev-en

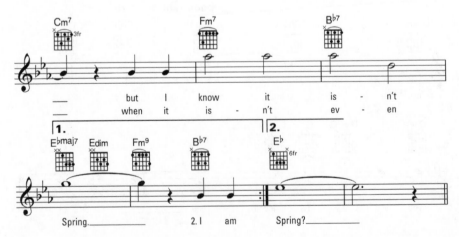

1.
Spring.

2.
2. I am Spring?

I keep wish-ing I were some-where else,____ walk-ing down a strange new street,____ hear-ing words that I have nev-er heard____ from a man I've yet to meet.____ I'm as bus-y as a spi-der spin-ning day-dreams,____ I'm as gid-dy as____ a ba-by on a swing.____ I

The Impossible Dream

Words by Joe Darion
Music by Mitch Leigh

1. To dream___ the im-pos-si-ble
(2.) right___ the un-right-a-ble

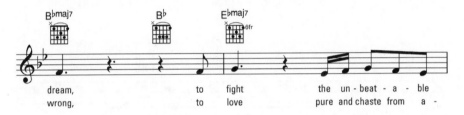

dream, to fight the un-beat-a-ble
wrong, to love pure and chaste from a-

foe, to bear___ with un-bear-a-ble sor-row, to
-far, to try___ when your arms are too wea-ry, to

1.
run___ where the brave dare not go. 2. To

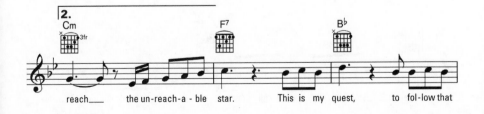

2.
reach___ the un-reach-a-ble star. This is my quest, to fol-low that

117

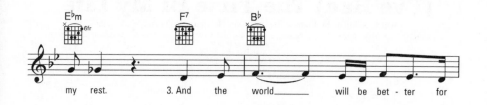

my rest. 3. And the world_____ will be bet - ter for

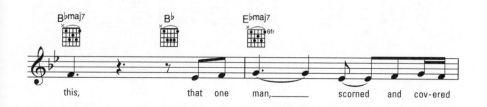

this, that one man,_____ scorned and cov-ered

with scars,_____ still_____ strove_____ with his last ounce of

molto rit.

cour - age,_____ to reach the un - reach - a - ble

a tempo

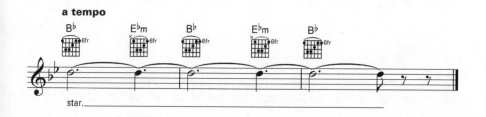

star._____

(I've Had) The Time Of My Life

Words & Music by Frankie Previte, John DeNicola & Donald Markowitz

I've___ had___ the time of my life,___ no I nev-

- er felt___ this way be - fore, yes I swear it's the truth___

1.

_____ and I owe it all to you.___

2.

(J) 2. With my owe it all to you,__ 'cause

I've had the time of my life,___ and I've

searched through ev - 'ry o - pen door till I've found the___ truth

_____ and I owe it all to you.___

122

Sax solo

(B) Now I've had the time of my life_____ no I nev - er felt_ this way be - fore, yes I swear_ _ it's the truth,_____ and I owe_ it all to you._

(Both) I've had the time of my life_____ no I nev -
I've had the time of my life_____ and I've searched

- er felt_ this way be - fore, yes I swear it's the truth,_
_ through ev - 'ry o - pen door till I've found the truth,_

Repeat to fade

_____ and I owe it all to you._ 'cause_
_____ and I owe it all to you._ 'cause_

123

June Is Bustin' Out All Over

Words by Oscar Hammerstein II
Music by Richard Rodgers

♩ = 120

1. June   is   bust - in'   out   all   ov - er!_____
2. June   is   bust - in'   out   all   ov - er!_____
3. June   is   bust - in'   out   all   ov - er!_____

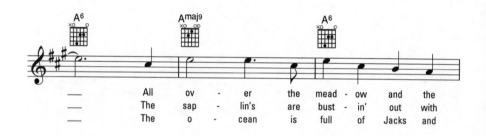

___   All   ov - er   the   mead - ow   and   the
___   The   sap - lin's are   bust - in'   out   with
___   The   o - cean   is   full   of   Jacks   and

hill!_____   Buds   're   bust - in'   out - ta
sap!_____   Love   hes   found   my   bro - ther
Jills._____   With   her   lit - tle   tail   a -

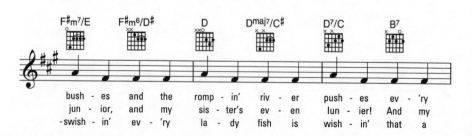

bush - es   and   the   romp - in'   riv - er   push - es   ev - 'ry
jun - ior,   and   my   sis - ter's   ev - en   lun - ier!   And   my
-swish - in'   ev - 'ry   la - dy   fish   is   wish - in'   that   a

lit - tle wheel that wheels be - side a mill!____
ma is get - tin' kit - ten - ish with pap!____
male would come and grab her by the gills!____

June is bust - in' out all ov - er!____ The
June is bust - in' out all ov - er!____ To
June is bust - in' out all ov - er!____ The

feel - in' is get - tin' so in - tense,____ that the
la - dies the men are pay - in' court.____ Lots - a
sheep are - n't sleep - in' an - y more!____ All the

young Vir - gin - ia creep - ers hev been hug - gin' the be -
ships are kept at an - chor jest be - cause the Cap - tains
rams that chase the ewe sheep are de - ter - mined there'll be

-jeeb - ers out - a all the morn - in' glo - ries on the
hank - er fer a com - fort they ken on - ly get in
new sheep and the ewe sheep are - n't ev - en keep - in'

fence!_____ Be - cause it's June!_____ June, June, June.
port!_____ Be - cause it's June!_____ June, June, June.
score!_____ On a-count-a it's June!_____ June, June, June.

1, 2. *rit.*

Jest be - cause it's June! June! June!_____
Jest be - cause it's June! June! June!_____
Jest be - cause it's June! June!

Fresh and a - live and gay and young, June is a love song sweet-ly sung._
June makes the bay look bright and new, sails gleam - 'in white on sun - lit blue._

3.

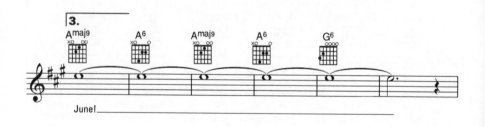

June!_____

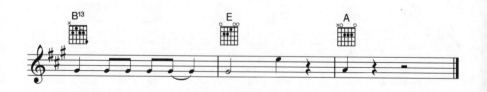

126

The Lambeth Walk

Words by Douglas Furber & Arthur Rose
Music by Noel Gay

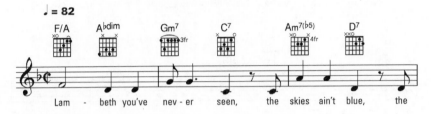

Lam - beth you've nev - er seen, the skies ain't blue, the

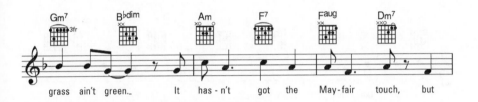

grass ain't green._ It has-n't got the May-fair touch, but

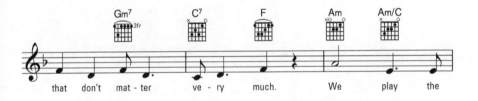

that don't mat - ter ve - ry much. We play the

Lam - beth way, not like you, but a bit more gay. And

when we have_ a bit of fun.__ Oh, boy!__

128

do   as you   darn___   well   pleas - ey,   why don't   you make   your

way   there,   go   there,   stay   there.

Once   you   get___   down   Lam - beth   way,___

ev - 'ry   eve - ning,   ev - 'ry   day;___

you'll   find   your - self   do - in'   the   Lam - beth

1.

walk.

2.

walk.

HAROLD PRINCE

in association with RUTH MITCHELL
presents

ALEXIS
SMITH

GENE
NELSON

DOROTHY
COLLINS

JOHN
McMARTIN

FOLLIES
A NEW MUSICAL
also starring
YVONNE DE CARLO

Losing My Mind

Follies was always a problematic, shifting musical, subject to many re-writes involving changes of mood and emphasis as it made its way from Broadway in 1971 via Los Angeles, and New York's Lincoln Center to London's West End. A movie is at last in production at the time of this writing. *Follies* was Stephen Sondheim's bid to rehabilitate himself by writing both music and lyrics himself after the bad experience of *Do I Hear A Waltz?*, a failed show for which he had supplied lyrics for Richard Rodgers' music. Sondheim had written both words and music before in *A Funny Thing Happened On The Way To The Forum* but he was now looking to create something more sophisticated. The premise of *Follies* was a reunion of a Ziegfeld-type troupe of dancing girls in the theatre where they once performed in a show called *Weissman's Follies*. The derelict venue is now about to be demolished. Immersed in a sustained mood of nostalgia and regret the now mature ex-cast members are constantly confronted by their younger selves whose personal follies are re-enacted before

them to add extra poignancy to the show's title. An ambitious concept, *Follies* has become something of a cult musical even if it never seemed quite finished to its author's satisfaction. James Goldman had written the book of the show and was occasionally invited to tweak it by Sondheim, sometimes in response to a producer's requests. The original Broadway ending was made more upbeat for the London version and since 1971 songs have been intermittently added to and subtracted from the show. *Follies* can also be considered post-modern in that much of its score is a superior pastiche of the sort of vaudeville-style music being celebrated at the reunion. Intercut are more contemporary book numbers and, as ever, Sondheim's lyrics are urbane, elegant and incisively intelligent throughout. Several of the show's songs took on a life of their own for people who had never even seen the show, but the highest profile hit came from the penultimate 'Loveland' sequence in which all the young versions of the performers frenetically re-enact their youthful mistakes in a theatrical parody of *Weissman's Follies* gone mad. Sally Durant (originally played by Dorothy Miller) appears in this sequence as a torch singer to perform 'Losing My Mind'. Who would have thought that this bitter-sweet introspective number would eventually make the charts in a thumping electronic version produced by The Pet Shop Boys and featuring Liza Minelli?

Losing My Mind

Words & Music by Stephen Sondheim

© Copyright 1971 Herald Square Music Company, USA.
Carlin Music Corporation.
All Rights Reserved. International Copyright Secured.

Freely ♩ = 70

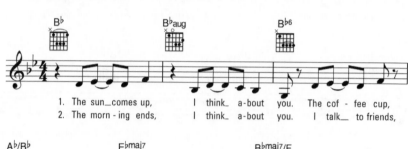

1. The sun__comes up, I think__ a-bout you. The cof - fee cup,
2. The morn - ing ends, I think__ a-bout you. I talk__ to friends,

I think__ a-bout you. I want you so, it's like I'm los-ing my mind.__
I think__ a-bout you. And do they know it's like I'm los-ing my mind?__

All af - ter-noon do - ing ev - 'ry lit-tle chore, The thought of you stays

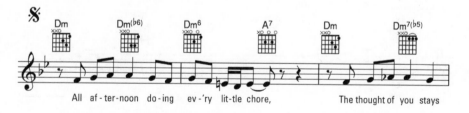

bright. Some - times I stand in the

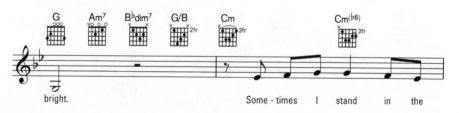

131

mid-dle of the floor, not go-ing left, not go-ing right.

3. I dim the lights and think a-bout you. Spend sleep-less nights

to think a-bout you. You said you loved me

or were you just be-ing kind, or am I los-ing my

mind?

1.

I want you so, it's like I'm los-ing my
Does no one know

Love Never Dies

Music by Andrew Lloyd Webber
Lyrics by Glenn Slater
Arranged by David Cullen

Who knows when love be - gins? Who knows what makes it start? One

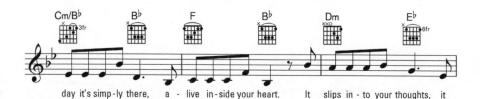

day it's simp - ly there, a - live in - side your heart. It slips in - to your thoughts, it

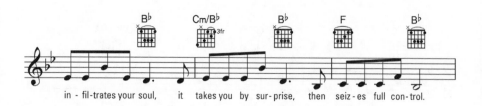

in - fil - trates your soul, it takes you by sur - prise, then seiz - es full con - trol.

Try to de - ny it, and try to pro - test, but

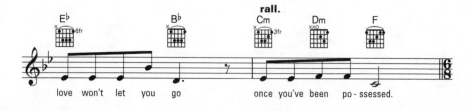

love won't let you go once you've been po - ssessed.

a tempo

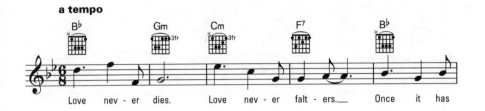

Love nev-er dies. Love nev-er falt-ers.__ Once it has

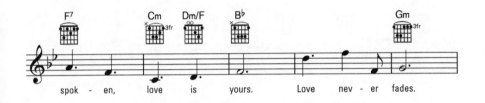

spok - en, love is yours. Love nev - er fades.

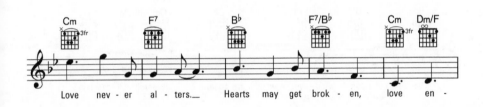

Love nev - er al - ters.__ Hearts may get brok - en, love en -

dures... Hearts may get brok - en, love en - dures.__ And

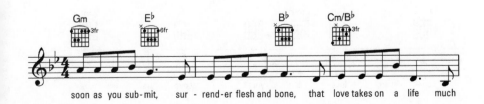

soon as you sub-mit, sur - rend-er flesh and bone, that love takes on a life much

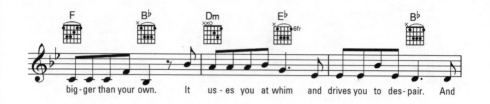

big-ger than your own. It us-es you at whim and drives you to des-pair. And

forc-es you to feel more joy than you can bear. Love gives you pleas-ure, and

love brings you pain! And yet, when both are gone, love will still re-main.

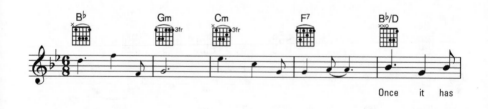

Once it has

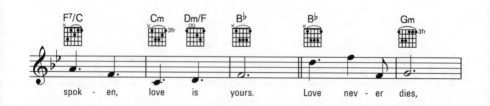

spok-en, love is yours. Love nev-er dies,

Love never alters,— hearts may get brok-en love en-dures... Hearts may get brok-en... Love nev-er dies! Love will con-ti-nue!— Love keeps on beat-ing when you're gone! Love nev-er dies once it is in you!— Life may be fleet-ing, love lives on... Life may be fleet-ing, love lives on.

137

Luck Be A Lady

Words & Music by Frank Loesser

Freely (♩ = 92)

They call you La - dy Luck, but there is room for doubt. At

times you have a ve - ry un - la - dy - like way of run - ning out.___ You're

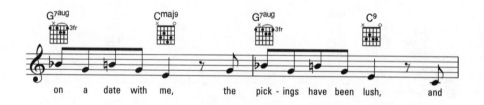

on a date with me, the pick - ings have been lush, and

yet be - fore this eve - ning is ov - er you might give me the brush. You

might for - get your man - ners, you might re - fuse to stay, and

way you've treat - ed oth - er guys you've been with, luck be a

la - dy with me._____

A

{ la - dy does - n't leave her es - cort,_____ it is - n't
{ la - dy would - n't flirt with stran - gers,_____ she'd have a

fair,_____ it is - n't nice._____ A la - dy does - n't
heart,_____ she'd have a soul._____ A la - dy would - n't

wan - der all ov - er the room and blow on some
make lit - tle snake - eyes at me, when I've bet my

oth - er guy's dice._____ }
life on this roll._____ }

So

let's keep the par - ty po - lite,_____ nev - er get

out of my sight,_____ stick with me ba - by I'm the

fel - low you came in with, luck be a la - dy,

luck be a la - dy,

1.

luck be a la - dy to - night._____

2.

luck be a la - dy_____ to - night!_____

Love Changes Everything

Music by Andrew Lloyd Webber
Lyrics by Don Black & Charles Hart

name. / shame.
No - thing in the world will ev - er be the

1.
same.

2.
same.____ *(Strings cue)*

Off____ in - to the world we go, plan - ning

fu - tures, shap - ing years. Love____ bursts in and

sud - den - ly, all our wis - dom dis - ap - pears.

144

Maybe This Time

Words by Fred Ebb
Music by John Kander

145

ev-'ry-bo-dy, oh, they love a win-ner, so no-bo-dy loved

me. La-dy Peace-ful, La-dy Hap-py,

that's what I___ longed to be. Well all the odds are

there in my fa-vour, some-thing's bound_ to be-gin. It's got-ta hap-pen,

hap-pen some-time, may-be this time, may-be this time I'll

win._____

147

My Favourite Things

If the movies of stage musicals are often seen more as useful records than defining versions, *The Sound of Music* might be said to have reversed that trend. It almost comes as a surprise to recall that Rodgers and Hammerstein's final musical started life on Broadway in 1959 starring Mary Martin (the original Nelly Forbush in, *South Pacific*) and Vienna-born folk singer and character actor Theodore Bikel. It had been inspired by a 1956 West German film about the von Trapp family and would itself become adapted into a hugely successful Austrian-set film starring Julie Andrews as Maria the dithering nun and Christopher Plummer as her militaristic widowed employer Georg von Trapp, a man who has so many children he doesn't know what to do. In retrospect it is hard not to see *The Sound of Music* as a late softening of Rodgers and Hammerstein's style. Although loosely based on a true story and not short of villains (after all, towards the end there is nothing much between the Nazis and Austria except Maria's formidable

soprano voice) it still seems more sentimental and less muscular than *Carousel*, *Oklahoma! The King and I* or *South Pacific*. Even so *The Sound Of Music* probably generated more hit songs than any other musical, largely due to the popularity of the film version. Richard Rodgers wrote both melody and lyrics to two more songs for inclusion in the 1965 film (Hammerstein had died in 1960) but there were already plenty of tuneful numbers to accompany this feel-good story of the ex-convent governess and the retired military man groping their awkward way towards marriage against the backdrop of history. 'My Favourite Things' reworks the same idea as 'I Whistle A Happy Tune' from *The King and I* . Maria's list of cherished things is designed to cheer her up when things look bad. With the Anschluss imminent things are looking very bad indeed, but — in the film at least — Maria sings the song to the children in her charge to alleviate their fear of a storm rather than a fear of stormtroopers. A 1985 London revival saw Petula Clark, then in her fiftieth year, heroically tackling the part of Maria (age 19) to considerable acclaim. A 2006 London revival cast aspiring actress Connie Fisher, chosen via a reality TV talent show.

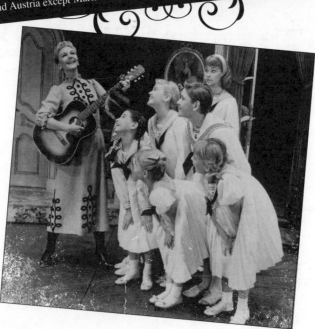

My Favourite Things

Words by Oscar Hammerstein
Music by Richard Rodgers

Original key: E♭ major

♩. = 70

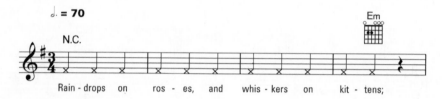

Rain - drops on ros - es, and whis - kers on kit - tens;

bright cop - per ket - tles and warm wool - len mit - tens; brown pa - per

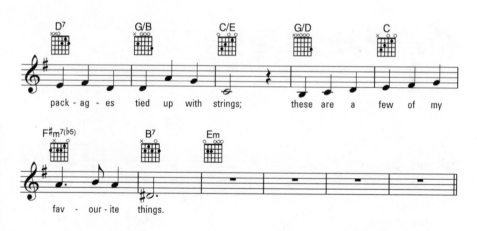

pack - ag - es tied up with strings; these are a few of my

fav - our - ite things.

Cream col - oured pon - ies and crisp ap - ple stru - dels; door - bells and

When the dog bites, when the bee stings,

when I'm feel - ing sad,_____ I

sim - ply re - mem - ber my fav - our - ite things, and

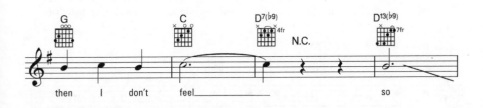

then I don't feel_____ so

bad._____

Night Fever

Words & Music by Barry Gibb, Maurice Gibb & Robin Gibb

♩ = 110

1. Lis - ten to___ the ground, there is move-ment all___ a - round, there is
(D.C.) (2.) heat of our___ love, don't need no help for us to make it. Gim - me

some - thing go - ing down and I can feel it. On the
just e - nough to take___ us to the morn - ing. I got

waves of___ the air, there is danc - ing out___ there, if it's
fire in___ my mind, I got high - er in___ my walk - ing and I'm

some - thing we can share, we can steal it. } And that
glow - ing in the dark, I give you warn - ing. }

sweet ci - ty wo - man, she moves through the light,___ con -

-troll - ing my mind___ and my soul.___ When you

reach out for me,___ yeah, and the feel - ing is___ bright.__ Then I get

night fe - ver, night fe - ver,___ we know how to do it.

Gim - me that night fe - ver, night fe - ver,___

___ we know how to show it.

Here I am, pray - ing for this mo - ment to last,___

liv - ing on the mu - sic so fine,___

born on the wind,___ mak - ing it mine.___

Night fe - ver, night fe - ver,___

we know how to do it.

Gim - me that night fe - ver, night fe - ver,___ we know how to

show it.

2. In the

(Repeat chorus to fade)

154

No Matter What

Music by Andrew Lloyd Webber
Lyrics by Jim Steinman

♩ = 100

1. No mat-ter what they tell us, no mat-ter what they do,
2. If on-ly tears were laugh-ter, if on-ly night was day,

no mat-ter what they teach us, what we be - lieve is true.
if on - ly pray - ers were answered, then we would hear God say.

No mat-ter what they call us, how-ev - er they at - tack,
No ma - ter what they tell you, no mat-ter what they do,

no mat-ter where they take us, we'll find our own way back.___
no mat-ter what they teach you, what you be-lieve is true.___ And

can't de - ny___ what I___ be - lieve,_ I can't be___ what I'm not.
I will keep_ you safe___ and strong and shel - tered_ from the storm.

155

I know our love's for - ev - er,
No mat - ter where it's bar - ren

I know no mat - ter what.
our dream is be - ing born.

3. No mat-ter who they fol - low, no mat-ter where they lead,

no mat-ter how they judge us, I'll be ev-'ry-one you need. No

156

matter if__ the sun__ don't shine,_____ or if the__ skies are blue.__

No mat-ter what the end-ing, my life be-gan with you. I

can't de-ny__ what I____ be-lieve, I can't be__ what I'm not.__

I know this love's for-ev-er. That's all that mat-ters now no mat-ter

what. No no mat - ter what. No no mat -

- ter what._____ No no mat - ter what.

Ol' Man River

Words by Oscar Hammerstein II
Music by Jerome Kern

Old man riv - er, dat old man riv - er, he must know sump - in', but

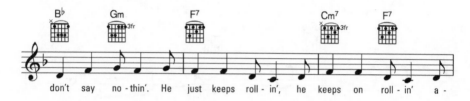

don't say no - thin'. He just keeps roll - in', he keeps on roll - in' a -

- long.   He don't plant 'ta - ters, he don't plant cot - ton, an'

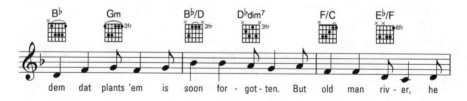

dem dat plants 'em is soon for - got - ten. But old man riv - er, he

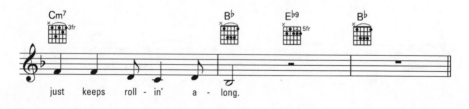

just keeps roll - in' a - long.

Once In Love With Amy

Words & Music by Frank Loesser

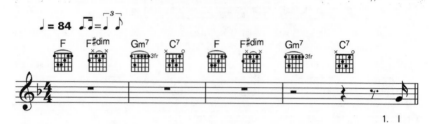

1. I

saw you,___ sir, hav - ing a look at___ her___ as
(2.) warn you,___ sir, don't start to dream of ___ her,___ just

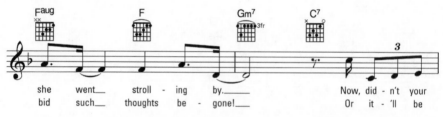

she went___ stroll - ing by._____ Now, did - n't your
bid such___ thoughts be - gone!_____ Or it - 'll be

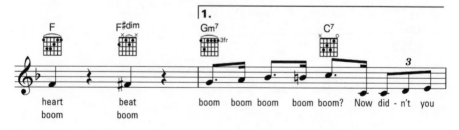

1.

heart beat boom boom boom boom boom? Now did - n't you
boom boom

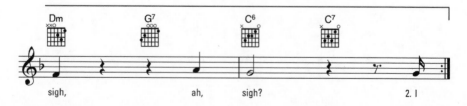

sigh, ah, sigh? 2. I

160

161

Once____ in love____ with Am - y,

al - ways____ in love____ with Am - y;____

ev - er____ and ev - er____ sweet - ly you'll ro-mance her.____

Trou - ble is the ans - wer____ will be that

Am - y'd ra - ther stay in love with

1.
me.

2.
me.

One

Words by Edward Kleban
Music by Marvin Hamlisch

One Night In Bangkok

Words & Music by Benny Andersson, Tim Rice & Bjorn Ulvaeus

♩ = 110

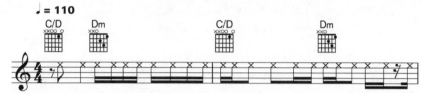

(The   1. Bang-kok! O - ri-en-tal set-ting and the   ci-ty don't know what the ci-ty is get-ting. The
American) 2.   Si-am's gon-na be the wit-ness to the   ul-ti-mate test of   ce-re-bral fit-ness.

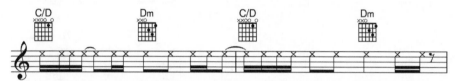

crème de la crème_ of the chess world in   a   show_ with ev-'ry-thing but   Yul   Bryn - ner.
This grips me   more than would a   mud-dy old riv-er or re-clin-ing Bud-dah.

(1° tacet) - |
And thank God I'm on - ly watch-ing the   game   con-trol-ling it.

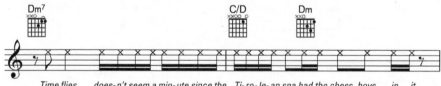

Time flies   does-n't seem a min-ute since the Ti-ro-le-an spa had the chess boys   in   it.
I don't   see you guys rat-ing   the   kind of mate I'm   con-tem-plat-ing. I'd

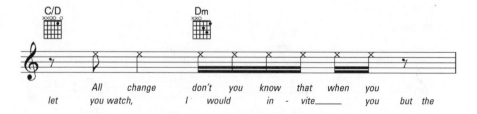

    All   change   don't you know that when you
let   you watch,   I   would   in - vite_____ you but the

play at this lev-el there's no or-di-na-ry ven-ue. It's Ice - land_ or the
queens we use would___ not ex-cite you. So_ you'd bet-ter go back to your

Phil - ip - pines___ or Hast - ings or___ or this place!__
bars, your tem-ples, your mas - sage par - lours –

(Choir) One night in Bang - kok and the world's your___

oys - ter, the bars are tem-ples but the pearls ain't free.___

To Coda

You'll find a god_ in ev-ery gold - en___ clois-ter and if you're

luck-y then the god's a she.___ I can feel an an - gel slid-ing up to me.___

167

(The One town's ve - ry like an - oth - er when your
American)
head's down ov - er your pie - ces, bro - ther. (Choir) It's a
drag, it's a bore, it's real-ly such a pi-ty to be look-ing at the board, not look-ing at the ci-ty.
(The Whad-dy - a mean? You've seen one crowd - ed, pol - lu - ted, stink - ing town.__
American)
(Choir) Tea, girls_warm and sweet some are set up in the Som-er - set Maug-ham suite.
(The Get Thai'd! You're talk-ing to a tour-ist whose ev-'ry move's a - mong the pur - est,
American)
I get__ my kicks a - bove the waist-line, sun-shine!

(Choir) One night in Bang-kok makes a hard man hum-ble, not much be-tween despair and ec-sta-sy. One night in Bang-kok and the tough guys tum-ble, can't be too care-ful with your com-pa-ny I can feel the dev-il walk-ing next to me.

1.

2. *D.S. al Coda*

(Flute solo on scale)

169

Promises, Promises

Words by Hal David
Music by Burt Bacharach

♩ = 145

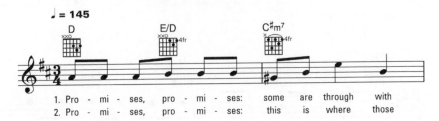

1. Pro - mi - ses, pro - mi - ses: some are through with
2. Pro - mi - ses, pro - mi - ses: this is where those

pro - mi - ses, pro - mi - ses now. I don't know how
pro - mi - ses, pro - mi - ses end. I won't pre - tend

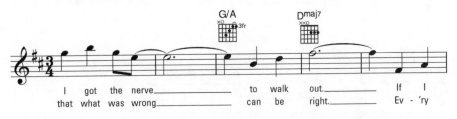

I got the nerve_____ to walk out._____ If I
that what was wrong_____ can be right._____ Ev - 'ry

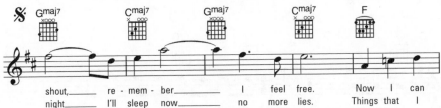

shout,_____ re - mem - ber_____ I feel free. Now I can
night_____ I'll sleep now_____ no more lies. Things that I

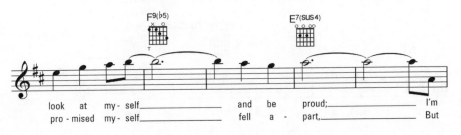

look at my - self_____ and be proud;_____ I'm
pro - mised my - self_____ fell a - part,_____ But

laugh - ing out loud._____ Oh,

I found my heart._____ Oh,

pro - mi - ses, their kind of pro - mi - ses, can just des -

- troy your___ life._____ Oh, pro - mi - ses, those kind of

pro - mi - ses, take all the joy from___ life._____ Oh,

pro - mi - ses, pro - mi - ses, my kind of pro - mi - ses_____

can lead to joy and hope and love:_____

172

yes, love.

(Trumpet)

D.S. al Coda (as 2°)

Ev - 'ry

Coda

love: yes, love.

Repeat to fade

173

The Perfect Year

Music by Andrew Lloyd Webber
Lyrics by Don Black & Christopher Hampton

(Norma) 1. Ring out the old, ring in the new, a mid-night wish, to share with

you. Your lips are warm, my head is light, were we a - live be - fore to -

night? I don't need a crow-ded ball - room, ev - 'ry-thing I want is

here, if you're with me, ___ next year will be ___ the per-fect year. (Joe) 2. Be-fore we

play ___ some dan-g'rous game, ___ be - fore we fan ___ some harm-less

flame, we have to ask ___ if this is wise, ___ and if the game ___ is worth the

174

prize. With this wine, and with this mu-sic, how can a-ny-thing be

clear? Let's wait and see,_____ it may just be_____ the per-fect

year. *(Norma)* 3. It's New Year's Eve, and hopes are

high, dance one year in, kiss one good-bye, a-noth-er chance, an-oth-er

start, so ma-ny dreams to tease the heart. We don't need a crow-ded

ball - room, ev-'ry-thing we want is here, and face to

face_____ we will em-brace_____ the per-fect year.

The Phantom Of The Opera

Andrew Lloyd Webber's musical take on Gaston Leroux's lurid early 20th century novel was by far the most commercially successful of numerous adaptations, many of which seemed to do better than the original novel which always sold poorly. The 1925 American film version with Lon Chaney was famous for Chaney's self-applied make-up and, according to its poster, a cast of 5,000. A loose musical movie adaptation — Brian De Palma's *Phantom of the Paradise* — was made in 1974, although this was only partially based on the original plot, throwing in bits of the Faust legend and various other literary and cinematic references. There have been many more adaptations, but it was Lloyd Webber's 1986 version that hit the jackpot. Opening in London it originally starred Michael Crawford as Erik the Phantom and Sarah Brightman as the object of his desire Christine Daaé. Its triumph in London, on Broadway and around the world has made it the greatest commercial success ever enjoyed by a single media enterprise. Lloyd Webber's original choice of lyricist was not straight-forward; the legendary Alan Jay Lerner contributed just one song ('Masquerade') but was in ill-health after a string of Broadway failures and personal setbacks. He died soon afterwards. Richard Stilgoe took over but much of what he wrote was later revamped by Charles Hart. An obvious difficulty facing any popular musical with an operatic setting is which way to go with the music. Lloyd Webber chose to keep the operatic flavour throughout, with one notable exception: the title song 'Phantom of The Opera'. Performed in both Act 1 and Act 2 it is sung by Erik and Christine as he takes her by boat to his hiding place beneath the opera house, and it is an unashamedly dramatic pop song. Many cover versions have been made, ranging from orchestral treatments to a guitar version by Hank Marvin. Andrew Lloyd Webber's brother Julian performed an intricate cello version of the song specially arranged by the show's original orchestrator. Given the staggering ongoing success of *Phantom* it seems odd that Lloyd Webber chose to create a sequel, although he claimed *Love Never Dies* was a stand-alone show and not a sequel. Even so this 2010 musical sees the same principals relocated to Coney Island some ten years after their first dramatic adventure.

The Phantom Of The Opera

Music by Andrew Lloyd Webber
Lyrics by Charles Hart
Additional Lyrics by Richard Stilgoe & Mike Batt

(Christine) In sleep he sang to me,_____ in dreams he came, that voice which calls to me_____ and speaks my name. And do I dream a-gain?_____ for now I find_____ the phan - tom of the op-er-a is there_____ in -side my

mind.

(Phantom) Sing once a-

-gain with me____ our strange du - et;____ my pow - er

ov - er you____ grows strong - er yet. (8va basso) And though you

turn from me____ to glance be - hind,____ the

phan - tom of the op - er - a is there____ in - side your

mind.___

(Christine) Those who have seen your face___ draw back in

fear.___ I am the mask you wear,___ (Phantom) It's me they

hear.   (Both) { Your spi – rit and my voice___ in one com-
                      { My spi – rit and your voice___ in one com-

- bined;___ the phan – tom of the op – er – a is
- bined;___ the phan – tom of the op – er – a is

                    He's there,   the phan – tom of   the
there   in – side my mind.
there   in – side your mind.

op - era._____ Be - ware the phan - tom of the

op - era._____ (Phantom) In all your

fan - ta - sies,_____ you al - ways knew_____ that man and

mys - ter - y_____ (Christine) were both in you. (Both) { And in this
                                                              { And in this

la - by - rinth_____ where night is blind,_____ the phan -
la - by - rinth_____ where night is blind,_____ the phan -

- tom of the op - er - a is here_____ in - side my mind.
- tom of the op - er - a is there_____ in - side your mind.

180

The Rhythm Of Life

Words by Dorothy Fields
Music by Cy Coleman

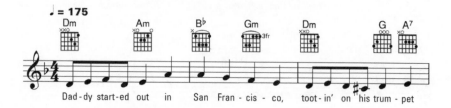

Dad-dy start-ed out in San Fran-cis-co, toot-in' on his trum-pet

loud and mean, Sud-den-ly a voice said, "Go forth, Dad-dy,

spread the pic-ture on a wid-er screen." And the voice said, "Dad-dy, there's a

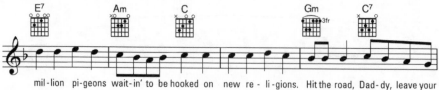

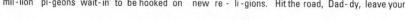

mil-lion pi-geons wait-in' to be hooked on new re-li-gions. Hit the road, Dad-dy, leave your

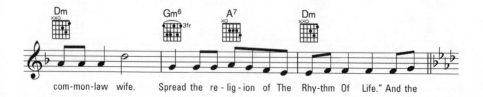

com-mon-law wife. Spread the re-lig-ion of The Rhy-thm Of Life." And the

tell them ev - 'ry - thing you know.

Dad - dy spread the gos - pel in Mil - wau - kee, took his walk - ie talk - ie to

Rock - y Ridge, blew his way to Can - ton, then to Scran - ton,

till he land - ed un - der the Man - hat - tan Bridge. Dad - dy was a new sen - sa - tion,

got him - self a con - gre - ga - tion, built up quite an op - er - a - tion

down be - low. With the pie - eyed pip - er blow - ing,

while the mus - ca - tel was flow - ing, all the cats were go, go, go - ing down be - low. Dad-dy was a new sen - sa - tion, got him-self a con - gre - ga - tion, built up quite an op - er - a - tion down_ be - low. With the pie - eyed pip - er blow - ing, while the mus - ca - tel was flow - ing, all the cats were go, go, go - ing down_ be - low. Flip your wings and fly to Dad - dy, flip your wings and

185

fly to Dad - dy, flip your wings and fly to Dad - dy,

fly,___ fly,___ fly to Dad - dy. Take a dive and swim to Dad - dy,

take a dive and swim to Dad - dy, take a dive and

swim to Dad - dy, swim,___ swim,___ swim to Dad - dy.

To feel The Rhy-thm Of Life, to feel the pow-er-ful beat, to feel the

rhy-thm in your fin - gers, to feel the tin - gle in your feet.___

To feel The Rhy-thm Of Life, to feel the pow - er - ful beat, to feel the rhy-thm in your fin - gers, to feel the tin - gle in your feet._____

Dad - dy we got The Rhy-thm Of Life, of life, of life, of life. Yeah! Yeah! Yeah! Man!

Seasons Of Love

Words & Music by Jonathan Larson

Five hun-dred twen-ty-five thou-sand six hun-dred min - utes.

Five hun - dred twen - ty - five thou - sand mo - ments so dear.

Five hun - dred twen-ty-five thou - sand six hun - dred min - utes.

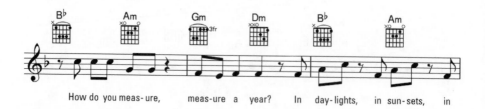

How do you meas-ure, meas-ure a year? In day-lights, in sun-sets, in

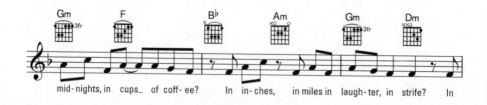

mid-nights, in cups_ of coff-ee? In in-ches, in miles in laugh-ter, in strife? In

five hun-dred twen-ty-five thou-sand six hun-dred min - utes. How

do you meas-ure, a year in the life? How a - bout

love?____ How a-bout love?____

How a - bout love?____

Mea-sure in love. Sea - sons of

love.____ Sea-sons of love.____

She Loves Me

Words by Sheldon Harnick
Music by Jerry Bock

191

Shoes Upon The Table

Words & Music by Willy Russell

1. Shoes up - on___ the ta - ble, and a spi - der's been killed.___

(Verse 2 see block lyrics)

Some - one broke the look - in' glass.____ There's a

full moon shin - in' and the salt's been____ spilled.

You're walk - in' on pave - ment cracks,___ don't know___ what's gon - na

come to pass.___ Now you know the de - vil's got your___

___ num - ber.___ You know he's gon - na find___ you, you know___

Verse 2:
Ain't no point in clutching at your rosary
You're always gonna know what was done
Even when you shut your eyes
You still see that you sold a son
And you can't tell anyone.

So Much Better

Words & Music by Laurence O'Keefe & Nell Benjamin

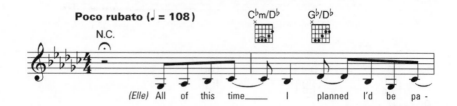

(Elle) All of this time___ I planned I'd be pa-

- tient and___ you would love___ me a - gain.___

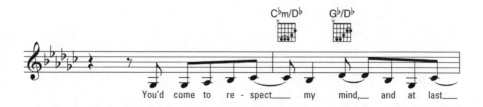

You'd come to re - spect___ my mind,___ and at last___

___ you'd find___ you could love___ me a - gain._____ And I have turned___

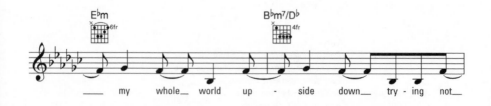

___ my whole___ world up - side down___ try - ing not___

to let you go. Watching you walk a - way is

♩ = 116

like a fa - tal blow. What? Whoa! Is that my name

up on that list? Does some-one know that I ex - ist?
up on that list, that beats the first time that we kissed!

Is this a mis - take? Am I ev - en a - wake?
You thought I was dumb, but I think that some -

Pinch me now to make sure. Ow! Yes! That is my name
- bod - y's judge-ment was poor! See-ing my name

in black and white! May-be I'm do - ing some-thing right.
in black and white like mak-in' love with you all night!

195

(3 Male Students) Ev -'ry night? *(Elle)* We said no - thing else__ could ev - er feel__ so right.__

D.S. al Coda

(Students) Well, this might! *(Elle)* Snap! See - in' my name__

Coda

__ No, wait! It feels so_____ much bet - ter. Hel - lo!__

__ Much bet- ter! It's Oh! Oh! Oh! Oh! Oh!__ Much bet- ter! 'Cause

I am so_____ much bet - ter than be - fore!__

*(Yes, she's so much bet - ter than__ be - fore.)*_____

May - be she's what you pre - fer,__ but hey, last year I was her.__

197

200

Sit Down, You're Rockin' The Boat

A near contemporary of *South Pacific*, *Guys and Dolls* was a very different sort of musical. Like *South Pacific* this 1950 show was based on several short stories, but in this instance these were written by Damon Runyon, comic chronicler of New York's Prohibition-era demi-monde where the only real crime was not to be colourful enough. The antics of Nathan Detroit, Miss Adelaide, Sky Masterson and Nicely-Nicely Johnson were based on three Runyon stories, 'Blood Pressure', 'Pick the Winner' and 'The Idyll Of Miss Sarah Brown'. Frank Loesser wrote both music and lyrics and the book was provided by Jo Swerling and Abe Burrows. The musical's story is essentially simple but its pace is frenetic and its characters are …well, Runyon-esque. Two apparently ill-starred romances feature in a plot largely concerned with gambling and hustling. No-longer-young Miss Adelaide is trying to get the ever-reluctant Nathan Detroit to marry her while reprobate Sky Masterson and pious Salvation Army mission leader Sarah Brown

appear to be an even less likely happy couple-in-waiting. The songs are of the highest quality and Loesser's comic masterpiece 'Adelaide's Lament' stands like a informal Brooklyn cousin to the best of W.S. Gilbert's droll lyrics. There was only one real show-stopper though. 'Sit Down, You're Rockin' the Boat' would be forever associated with Bernard Kotzin, professionally known as Stubby Kaye, who played Nicely-Nicely Johnson on Broadway, in London and in the 1950 movie of the show. His rousing number restates the show's main theme — religion v gambling & booze — in a dream-allegory about the stability of a boat on its way to Heaven being endangered by a solitary passenger still carrying dice and a bottle. Author Frank Loesser had already enjoyed a successful career as a songwriter in Hollywood before writing five musicals, of which *Guys and Dolls* became the most famous. Among his many hit songs was the award-winning 'Baby, It's Cold Outside' and these days his second best-known musical would be *How To Succeed In Business Without Really Trying*; it was revived in 2011 with Daniel Radcliffe cast in the role originally played by Robert Morse, latterly famous as Bert Cooper in AMC's *Mad Men*. 'Sit Down, You're Rockin' The Boat' was more recently featured in the 2009 pilot episode of Fox's TV hit show *Glee*.

Sit Down, You're Rockin' The Boat

Words & Music by Frank Loesser

Freely

1. I dreamed last night I got on the boat to Hea-ven, and
(2.) sailed a-way on that lit-tle boat to Hea-ven, and
(3.) as I laughed at those pas-sen-gers to Hea-ven, a

by some chance I had brought my dice a-long, and there I stood and I
by some chance found a bot-tle in my fist, and there I stood nice-ly
great big wave came and washed me ov-er-board, and as I sank, and I

hol-lered, "Some-one fade me." but the pas-sen-gers, they knew right from
pas-sin' out the whis-key, but the pas-sen-gers were bound to re-
hol-lered, "Some-one save me!" that's the mo-ment I woke up, thank the

♩ = 135

wrong. For the peo-ple all said, "Sit down,___ sit down,
- sist. For the peo-ple all said, "Be-ware,___ you're on___
Lord. And I said to my-self, "Sit down,___ sit down

___ you're rock-in' the boat."   Peo-ple all said, "Sit down,
___ a heav-en-ly trip."   Peo-ple all said, "Be-ware,
___ you're rock-in' the boat."   Said to my-self, "Sit down,

sit down,___ you're rock - in' the boat;___ and the
be - ware,___ you'll scut - tle the ship;___ and the
sit down,___ you're rock - in' the boat;___ and the

de - vil will drag you un - der by the sharp la - pel___ of your
de - vil will drag you un - der by the fan - cy tie___ 'round your
de - vil will drag you un - der with a soul so hea - vy you'd

check - ered coat;___ sit down,___ sit down,___ sit down,___
wick - ed throat;___ sit down,___ sit down,___ sit down,___
nev - er float;___ sit down,___ sit down,___ sit down,___

___ sit down,___ sit down,___ you're rock - in' the boat."___
___ sit down,___ sit down,___ you're rock - in' the boat."___
___ sit down,___ sit down,___ you're rock - in' the boat."___

2. I
3. And

203

Smoke Gets In Your Eyes

Words by Otto Harbach
Music by Jerome Kern

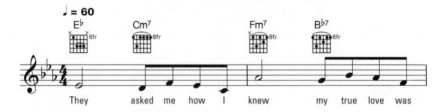

They asked me how I knew my true love was

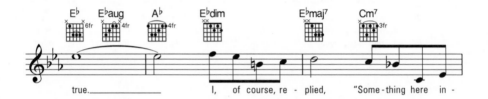

true.____ I, of course, re - plied, "Some-thing here in -

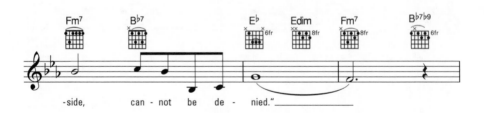

-side, can - not be de - nied."____

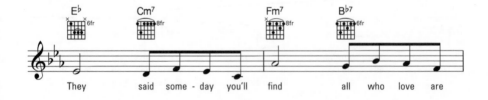

They said some - day you'll find all who love are

blind.____ When your heart's on fire, you must re - al -

-ize smoke gets in your eyes._____

So I chaffed__ them and I gai - ly laughed__ to think they could

doubt my love. Yet to - day____ my love has

flown a - way.__ I am with - out my love.

Now laugh - ing friends de – ride tears I can - not

hide._____ So I smile and say, "When a love - ly flame

dies, smoke gets in your eyes."_____

The Song Of Purple Summer

Words by Steven Sater
Music by Duncan Sheik

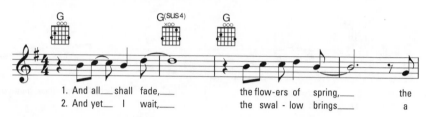

1. And all__ shall fade,__ the flow-ers of spring,__ the
2. And yet__ I wait,__ the swal-low brings__ a

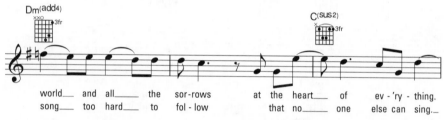

world__ and all__ the sor-rows at the heart__ of ev-'ry - thing.
song__ too hard__ to fol - low that no__ one else can sing._

— But still__ it stays,__ the but - ter - fly
— The fenc - es sway,__ the__ porch-es

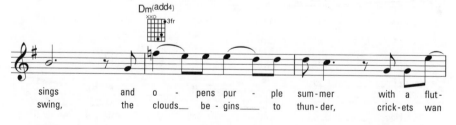

sings and o - pens pur - ple sum-mer with a flut-
swing, the clouds__ be - gins__ to thun- der, crick-ets wan

- ter of its wings.__ The earth__ will__
- der, mur - mur - ing.__ }

wave with corn,_____ the grey - fly_____ choir will

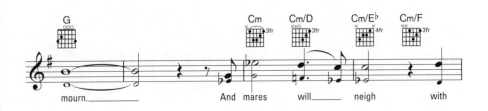

mourn._____ And mares will_____ neigh with

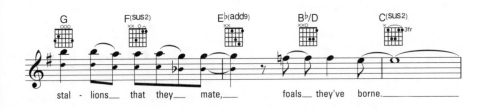

stal - lions___ that they___ mate,___ foals___ they've borne._____

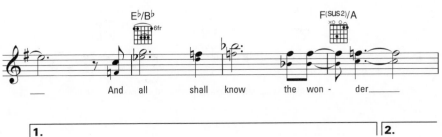

___ And all shall know the won - der_____

1.   **2.**

of pur - ple sum - mer._____

I_____ will sing the song___ of pur - ple sum -

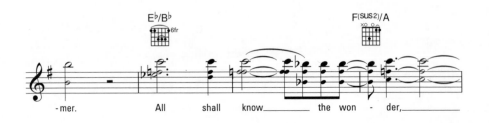

- mer. All shall know_____ the won - der,_____

___ I will sing the song___ of pur - ple sum -

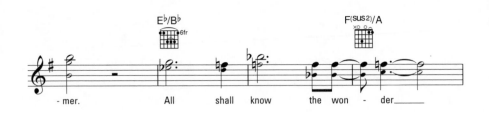

- mer. All shall know_____ the won - der_____

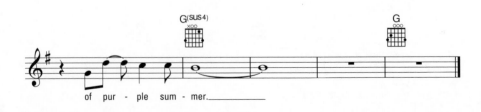

of pur - ple sum - mer._____

208

The Song That Goes Like This

Words by Eric Idle
Music by Eric Idle & John Du Prez

Bb   F/A
(D) Now we can go straight___   in - to   the mid-dle eight,___   a

Gm7   C(SUS4) C   F   F/A   Bb
bridge   that is   too   far for me.___ (L) I'll___ sing it in your face

A   Dm   G7   C   D
while we both em-brace (Both) and then   we change   the   key.___

G   D/F#
(D) Now we're in - to E,   that's awf-'ly high for me,   (L) but

Em   C   G   Em
ev-'ry-one_ can see   we should have stayed in D. (Both) For   this   is   our

Am7   D(SUS4)   D
song   that goes   like   this.___   (D) I'm

G   D/F#   B7/D#
feel-ing ve-ry proud, (L) you're sing-ing far too loud,___   (D) that's the

210

Springtime For Hitler

Words & Music by Mel Brooks

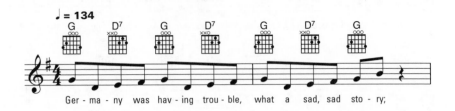

Ger - ma - ny was hav - ing trou - ble, what a sad, sad sto - ry;

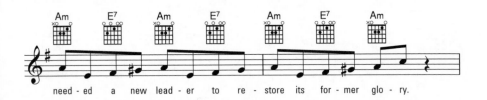

need - ed a new lead - er to re - store its for - mer glo - ry.

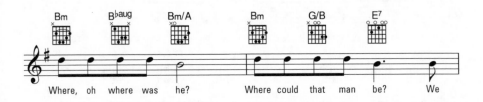

Where, oh where was he? Where could that man be? We

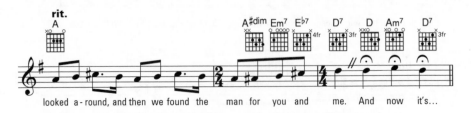

looked a - round, and then we found the man for you and me. And now it's...

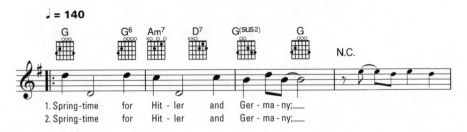

1. Spring - time for Hit - ler and Ger - ma - ny;___
2. Spring - time for Hit - ler and Ger - ma - ny;___

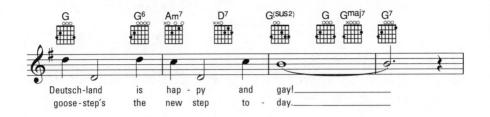

Deutsch-land   is   hap-py   and   gay!_____
goose-step's   the   new   step   to - day._____

We're march - ing   to   a   fast - er   pace;_____
Bombs fall - ing   from   the   skies   a - gain:_____

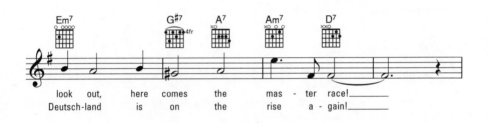

look   out,   here   comes   the   mas - ter   race!_____
Deutsch-land   is   on   the   rise   a - gain!_____

Spring-time   for   Hit - ler   and   Ger-ma - ny;
Spring-time   for   Hit - ler   and   Ger-ma - ny;

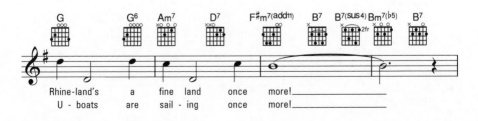

Rhine-land's   a   fine   land   once   more!_____
U - boats   are   sail - ing   once   more!_____

213

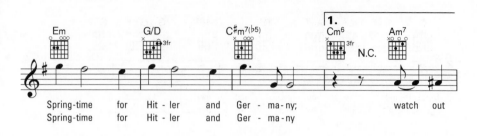

1.

Spring-time for Hit - ler and Ger - ma - ny; watch out
Spring-time for Hit - ler and Ger - ma - ny

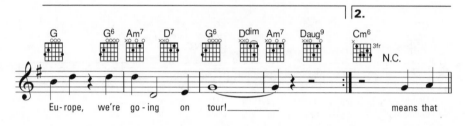

2.

Eu - rope, we're go - ing on tour!_____ means that

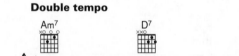

Double tempo

soon we'll be go - ing, we're got to be go - ing, you

know we'll be go - ing, you bet we'll be go - ing, you

Tempo I   *rit.*

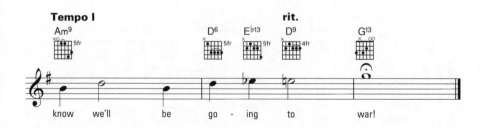

know we'll be go - ing to war!

Starlight Express

Music by Andrew Lloyd Webber
Lyrics by Richard Stilgoe

1. When your good - nights have been said,___ and you are
(2.) take me a - way,___ but bring me

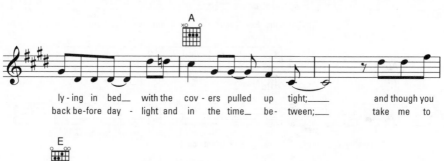

ly - ing in bed__ with the cov - ers pulled up tight;___ and though you
back be-fore day - light and in the time__ be- tween;___ take me to

count ev - 'ry sheep,_ you get the feel - ing that sleep__ is gon - na
ev - er - y- where,_ but don't a - ban - don me there__ just

stay a - way__ to - night.___ That's when you hear it com -
want to say__ I've been.___ I be - lieve in you com - plete -

- ing,___ that is when you hear the hum - ming of the }
- ly,___ though I may be dream - ing sweet - ly of the }

215

Star-light Ex - press.___ Star-light Ex - press,___ are you real,_____ yes or

no? Star-light Ex - press,_ ans-wer me yes;___ I

don't want you__ to__ go. 2. Want you to go.

(Harmonica)

And if you're there,_ and

if you know,_ then show me which_ way I_____ should go.___

217

Standing On The Corner

Words & Music by Frank Loesser

1. Stand - ing on the cor - ner watch - ing all the girls go by,

(Verses 2 & 3 see block lyrics)

stand - ing on the cor - ner watch - ing all the girls go

by. Bro - ther you don't know a nic - er oc - cu -

- pa - tion, mat - ter of fact nei - ther do I, than

stand - ing on the cor - ner watch - ing all the girls, watch - ing

To Coda

all the girls, watch - ing all the girls go by.

218

I'm the cat   that got the cream,   have-n't got a girl,—
Sat-ur-day   and I'm so broke,   could-n't buy a girl,—

but I   can dream.   Have-n't got a girl,—
a nick-el coke.   Still I'm liv-ing like—

but I   can wish, so   I   take me down to Main Street and
a mill-ion-aire, when I   take me down to Main Street and

that's where I se-lect my i-ma-gi-na-ry dish!
I   re-view the ha-rem pa-rad-ing for me there.

D.C. al Coda

✛ *Coda*

girls   go   by.

Verse 2:
Standing on the corner watching all the girls go by
Standing on the corner giving all the girls the eye
Brother if you've got a rich imagination
Give it a whirl, give it a try, try
Standing on the corner...

Verse 3:
Standing on the corner watching all the girls go by
Standing on the corner underneath a springtime sky
Brother you can't go to jail for what you're thinking
Or for the "wooo" look in your eye
You're only standing on the corner...

The Sun Has Got His Hat On

Words & Music by Ralph Butler & Noel Gay

♩ = 125

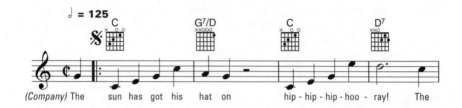

(Company) The sun has got his hat on hip - hip - hip - hoo - ray! The

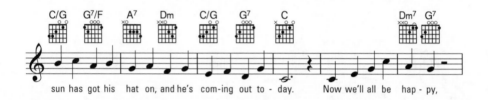

sun has got his hat on, and he's com-ing out to - day. Now we'll all be hap - py,

To Coda ⊕

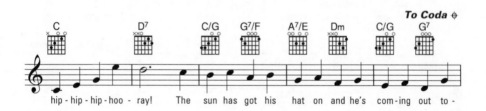

hip - hip - hip - hoo - ray! The sun has got his hat on and he's com-ing out to -

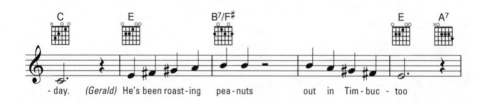

- day. (Gerald) He's been roast-ing pea-nuts out in Tim - buc - too

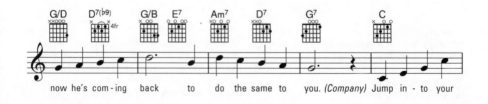

now he's com-ing back to do the same to you. (Company) Jump in - to your

Coda

(Gerald)All the lit-tle boys ex-ci-ted,   all the lit-tle girls de-
(2° Scat ad lib.)

-light-ed,   what a lot of sun for ev-'ry-one,

1.   **2.**

sit-ting in the sun all day.   day.   So jump in-to your

sun-bath   hip-hip-hip-hoo-ray!   The sun has got his

hat on and he's com-ing out,   he's com-ing out,

the sun has got his hat on and he's

com-ing out_____   to-day!

Supercalifragilisticexpialidocious

Words & Music by Richard M. Sherman & Robert B. Sherman

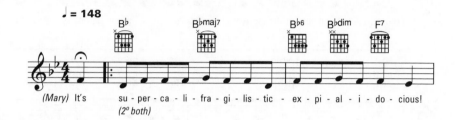

(Mary) It's su - per - ca - li - fra - gi - lis - tic - ex - pi - al - i - do - cious!
(2° both)

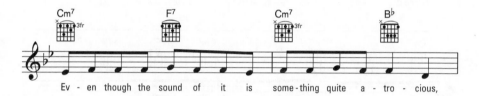

Ev - en though the sound of it is some - thing quite a - tro - cious,

if you say it loud e - nough you'll al - ways sound pre - co - cious:

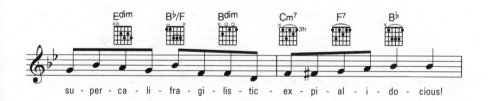

su - per - ca - li - fra - gi - lis - tic - ex - pi - al - i - do - cious!

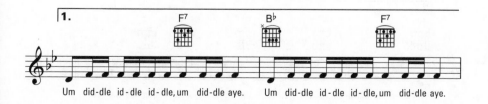

Um did-dle id-dle id-dle, um did-dle aye.   Um did-dle id-dle id-dle, um did-dle aye.

Um did-dle id-dle id-dle, um did-dle aye. Um did-dle id-dle id-dle, um did-dle aye. *(Bert)* Be-

- cause I was a - fraid to speak when I was just a lad, me

fa - ther gave me nose a tweak and told me I was bad. But

then one day I learned a word that saved my ach - ing nose, the

big - gest word you've ev - er heard, and this is how is goes: oh!

2.

Um did-dle id-dle id-dle, um did-dle aye. Um did-dle id-dle id-dle, um did-dle aye.

Um did-dle id-dle id-dle id-dle, um did-dle aye. Um did-dle id-dle id-dle id-dle, um did-dle aye. *(Mary)* He

tra - velled all a - round the world and ev - 'ry - where he went he'd

use his word and all would say "There goes a cle - ver gent!" *(Bert)* When

dukes and ma - ha - ra - jahs pass the time of day with me, I

say me spe - cial word and then they ask me out to tea. Oh!

(Both) Su - per - ca - li - fra - gi - lis - tic - ex - pi - al - i - do - cious!

225

Ev - en though the sound of it is some-thing quite a - tro - cious,

if you say it loud e - nough you'll al - ways sound pre - co - cious:

su - per - ca - li - fra - gi - lis - tic - ex - pi - al - i - do - cious!

Um did-dle id-dle id-dle, um did-dle aye. Um did-dle id-dle id-dle, um did-dle aye.

(Mary) Or you can say it backwards, which is: *dociousaliexpilisticfragicalirepus.*

But that's going a bit too far, don't you think?   *(Bert) Indubitably.*   *(Mary)* So

when the cat has got your tongue there's no need for dis - may, just

rit.

Dm⁷   G⁷   Dm⁷   G⁷   C

sum - mon up this word and then you've got a lot to say. But

Cmaj7   C⁷   F

bet - ter use it care - ful - ly, or it can change your life. *(Bert)* One

D   A⁷(SUS4)   F⁶   D⁷/F♯   G⁷
    N.C.   N.C.

night I said it to me girl, and now me girl's me wife! *(Both)* She's

a tempo

C   Cmaj7   C⁶   C♯dim   G⁷   Dm⁷   G⁷

su - per - ca - li - fra - gi - lis - tic - ex - pi - al - i - do - cious! Ev - en though the sound of it is

Dm⁷   G⁷   C   Cmaj7   C⁷   F

some - thing quite a - tro - cious, if you say it loud e - nough you'll al - ways sound pre - co - cious:

F♯dim   C/G   C♯dim   Dm⁷   G⁷   C

su - per - ca - li - fra - gi - lis - tic - ex - pi - al - i - do - cious!___

227

Superstar

Music by Andrew Lloyd Webber
Lyrics by Tim Rice

♩ = 124

(Judas) 1. Ev - 'ry - time I look at you I don't un - der - stand,__
2. Tell me what you think a - bout your friends at the top,__

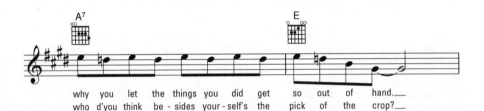

why you let the things you did get so out of hand.__
who d'you think be - sides your - self's the pick of the crop?__

You'd have man - aged bet - ter if you'd had__ it planned.
Bud - dah was he where it's at? Is he where you are?__

Why'd you choose such a back - ward time and such a strange land?__
Could Ma - hom - et__ move a moun - tain or was that just P. R.?

If you'd come to - day you would have reached a whole na - tion.
Did you mean to die like that? Was that a mis - take__ or

228

Is - ra - el in 4 B. C. had no mass com - mu - ni - ca - tion.
did you know your mess - y death would be a re - cord break - er?

(Choir) (Don't you get me wrong.)

(Don't you get me wrong.)

Don't you get me wrong.

A/G

(wrong now.) (Don't you get me

Don't you get me wrong.

A

(wrong.) (Don't you get me

Don't you get me wrong.

E7(♯9)

(wrong now.) (I on - ly want to

Don't you get me wrong.

E7

(know.) (I on - ly want to

On - ly want to know.

229

know now.)

(I on - ly want to

On - ly want to know.__

know.)

(I on- ly want to

know now.)

On - ly want to know.

On - ly want to know.

(Choir) Je - sus Christ,_ Je - sus Christ,_ who are you? What have you sa - cri-ficed?

Je - sus Christ Su - per-star,_ do you think you're what they say you are?_

Je - sus Christ_ Su - per - star,_ do you think you're what they

1.

say you are?_

230

say you are?

Je - sus Christ,_ Je - sus Christ,_ who are you? What have you sac - ri - ficed?_
(With ad. lib soul vocals)

Je - sus Christ,_ Je - sus Christ,_ who are you? What have you sac - ri - ficed?_

Je - sus Christ_ Su - per - star,_ do you think you're what they say you are?_

Je - sus Christ_ Su - per - star,_ do you think you're what they say you are?_

rit.

Are you what they say you are?

The Surrey With The Fringe On Top

Rarely can a song writing partnership have begun so successfully. True, Richard Rodgers and Oscar Hammerstein II had already individually collaborated with other partners on various successful shows, but together they would raise standards even further and in 1943 *Oklahoma!* set the bar high at their first attempt. The musical was based on a 1931 play, *Green Grow the Lilacs* and set in Oklahoma Territory in the year before statehood was granted. Two love stories, a tense rivalry between farmers and cowhands, a Persian charlatan selling fake love potions and a narrowly-avoided gruesome blinding combine to make *Oklahoma!* a full-blooded affair. Its main strength though was the songs. From the joyous opener 'Oh What A Beautiful Mornin'' through the slightly risqué 'Cain't Say No' and the exuberant 'The Farmer and The Cowman' to the wistful 'People Will Say We're In Love', all were superbly crafted songs perfectly pitched to advance the story. 'The Surrey with the Fringe on Top' was the show's second song, a piece of wishful thinking by hero Curly who is describing this elegant form of horse-drawn transport to ingénue Laurey as the only vehicle stylish enough for his dream date with her. A light song, it is still particularly well-crafted with clever internal rhymes and lyrics that reinforce the idea of briskly trotting horses. Over the years Curly has been played by several well-known performers even though for their first production Rodgers and Hammerstein requested little-known actors who could sing rather than famous singers who could act. (Their instincts were good because *Oklahoma!* changed expectations for musicals, introducing grit and substance to the performances). Alfred Drake was the first Curly, later going on to other leading roles in Broadway musicals. Howard Keel (then still called Harold) took on the role in London in 1947 where *Oklahoma!* was the first post-war musical to cross the Atlantic and received a rapturous, fourteen-encore welcome. A well-reviewed National Theatre production in 1998 cast Hugh Jackman in the role opposite Josefina Gabrielle as Laurey. *Oklahoma!*'s first run, back in 1943, ran for a record-breaking 2,212 performances and the 1955 movie with Gordon MacRae, Shirley Jones and Rod Steiger won an Academy Award.

The Surrey With The Fringe On Top

Words by Oscar Hammerstein II
Music by Richard Rodgers

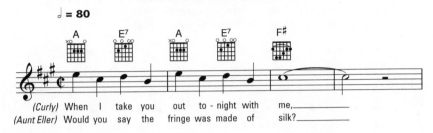

(Curly) When I take you out to - night with me,
(Aunt Eller) Would you say the fringe was made of silk?

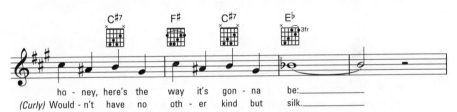

ho - ney, here's the way it's gon - na be:
(Curly) Would - n't have no oth - er kind but silk.

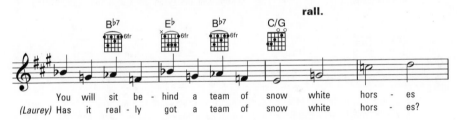

You will sit be - hind a team of snow white hors - es
(Laurey) Has it real - ly got a team of snow white hors - es?

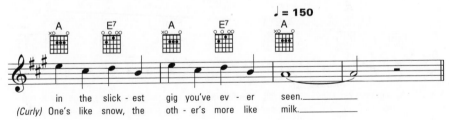

in the slick - est gig you've ev - er seen.
(Curly) One's like snow, the oth - er's more like milk.

1. Chicks and ducks and geese bet-ter scur-ry when I take you out in the sur-rey,
2. All the world-'ll fly in a flur-ry when I take you out in the sur-rey,
(Verse 3 see block lyrics)

233

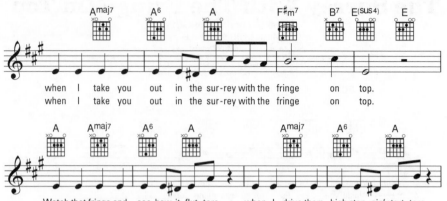

when I take you out in the sur-rey with the fringe on top.
when I take you out in the sur-rey with the fringe on top.

Watch that fringe and see how it flut-ters when I drive them high step-pin' strut-ters.
When we hit that road, hell for lea-ther, cha! Cats and dogs -'ll dance in the hea-ther,

Nos-ey pokes-'ll peek through their shut-ters and their eyes will pop. The
birds and frogs-'ll sing all to-ge-ther and the toads will hop. The

wheels are yel-ler, the up-hols-te-ry's brown, the dash-board's ge-nu-ine leath-er, with
wind-'ll whis-tle as we rat-tle a-long, the cows-'ll moo in the clov-er, the

i-sin-glass cur-tains you can roll right down in case there's a change in the weath-er.
riv-er will rip-ple out a whis-pered song and whis-per it ov-er and ov-er:

Two bright side-lights wink-in' and blink-in', ain't no fin-er rig I'm a-thin-kin'
Don't you wish you'd go on for-ev-er, don't you wish you'd go on for-ev-er,

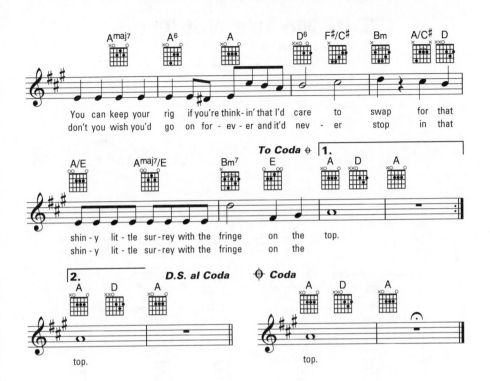

You can keep your rig if you're think- in' that I'd care to swap for that
don't you wish you'd go on for - ev - er and it'd nev - er stop in that

To Coda ⊕ | **1.**

shin - y lit - tle sur - rey with the fringe on the top.
shin - y lit - tle sur - rey with the fringe on the

2.

D.S. al Coda ⊕ **Coda**

top.

top.

Verse 3:
(More slowly and freely)
I can see the stars gettin' blurry
When we ride back home in the surrey
Ridin' slowly home in the surrey with the fringe on top
I can feel the day gettin' older
Feel a sleepy head near my shoulder
Noddin', droopin' close to my shoulder, till it falls ker-plop
The sun is swimmin' on the rim of a hill
The moon is takin' a header
And just as I'm thinkin' all the earth is still
A lark'll wake up in the medder
Hush, hush you bird, my baby's a-sleepin'
Maybe got a dream worth a-keepin'
Whoa! you team, and just keep a-creepin' at a slow clip-clop
Don't you hurry with the surrey with the fringe on the top.

Tell Me It's Not True

Words & Music by Willy Russell

1. Tell me it's not true. Say it's just a sto - ry,
2. Say it's just some clowns, two play-ers in the lime - light,

some - thing on the news. Tell me it's not true,
and bring the cur-tain down. Say it's just two clowns,

though it's here be - fore me. Say it's just a dream,
who could - n't get their lines right. Say it's just a show

say it's just a scene from an old mo - vie from years_ a - go;
on the ra - dio that we can turn ov - er and start a - gain;

from an old mo - vie of Ma - ri - lyn_ Mon - roe.
we can turn ov - er, it's on - ly_ a game.

236

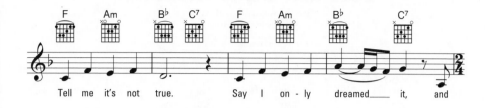

Tell me it's not true. Say I on-ly dreamed___ it, and

morn-ing will come soon. Tell me it's not true, say you did-n't

mean___ it. Say it's just pre-tend, say it's just the end___

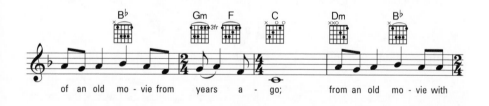

of an old mo-vie from years a - go; from an old mo-vie with

Ma - ri - lyn Mon - roe.___

Tell Me On A Sunday

Music by Andrew Lloyd Webber
Lyrics by Don Black

a tempo

G/F   C/E   Am   Dm   Dm⁷/G   Em   Am   Am/G

Don't leave in si - lence   With no word at all,   Don't get drunk and slam the door;

F   Am⁷   Dm   Em   **To Coda** ⊕   B♭   E♭   B♭

That's no way to end this; I   know how I   want you to   say good-bye.   Find a

                                                  D.C. al Coda

C/G   G⁷   F   B♭/F   F   C   G⁷   C

cir - cus ring   with a   fly-ing tra - peze,   Tell me   on   a   Sun-day   please.

⊕ **Coda**

B♭   E♭   B♭   Am⁷/G   G⁷

say good-bye;   don't run   off in the pour - ing rain; don't call

Am⁷/G   G⁷   Am⁷/G   F

me   as   they call your plane; take the   hurt out   of   all   the pain!   Take me

                                           rall.

C   G   F   B♭   F   C/G   G⁷   C

to   a   park   that's cov-ered with   trees.   Tell me   on   a   Sun - day   please.

239

There Is A Sucker Born Ev'ry Minute

Words by Michael Stewart
Music by Cy Coleman

min-ute   and I'm re-fer-rin' to the min-ute you was born.
min-ute,   but Ma'am you might of been the min-ute in be -

2. Each bless-ed   - tween.   If   I   al -

-low that right here in   my hands the   small-est liv-ing   hu-man man, the

sight of that is sure-ly worth a   dime.   If   I   pre-sent an e - du-ca-ted pooch who's

trained to dance_ the hooch-ie-cooch, what bet-ter way_ to waste a   bit of

time? If I im-port at mo-nu-ment-al cost a la-dy fair, who's head was lost while

cross-ing rail-road tracks to pick some zin-ni-as, who

has no ears or eyes or nose and wears pink tights in-stead of clothes, if

that ain't worth a buck my name ain't Phi-ne-as. Ah, you say that's hog-wash,

well who cares,— you'll buy my hog-wash long as there's... 3. A

suck-er born ev-'ry min-ute. Each time the se-cond hand— sweeps to the top, like

dan - de - li - ons up they pop, ears so big, eyes___ so wide. And

though my tale is bo - na - fide ba - lo - ney, just let me

spin it. And ain't no man who can re - sist me wait and

see, 'cause there's a sure - as - shoot - ing suck - er born___ a

min - ute and friends the big - gest one ex -

- clud - ing none is me.___

243

This Is My Jerry Springer Moment

Words & Music by Richard Thomas

♩ = 114

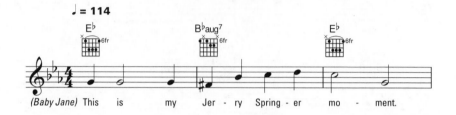

(Baby Jane) This is my Jer - ry Spring - er mo - ment.

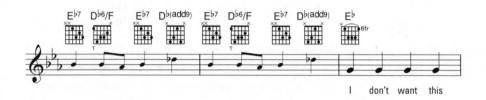

I don't want this

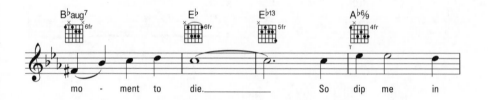

mo - ment to die. So dip me in

choc - 'late and throw me to the les - bi - ans,

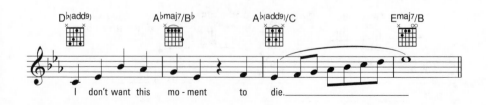

I don't want this mo - ment to die.

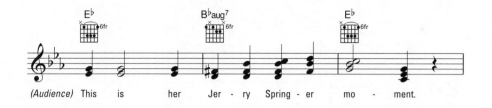

(Audience) This is her Jer - ry Spring - er mo - ment.

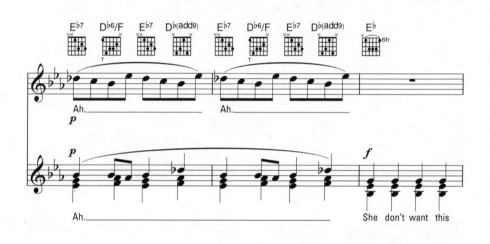

Ah.

p

Ah.

p

Ah.

f

She don't want this

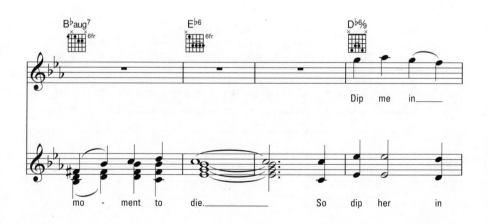

Dip me in

mo - ment to die. So dip her in

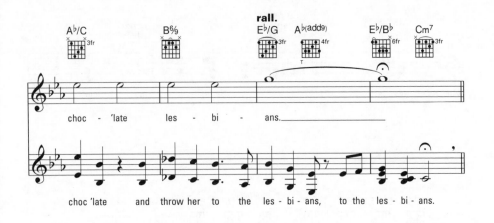

choc - 'late   les - bi - ans._____

choc 'late   and throw her to   the les - bi - ans,   to the les - bi - ans.

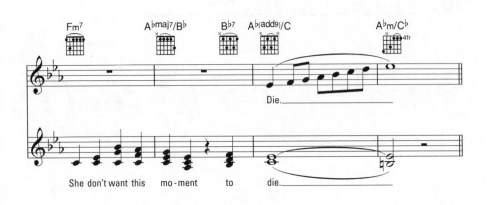

Die._____

She don't want this   mo-ment   to   die._____

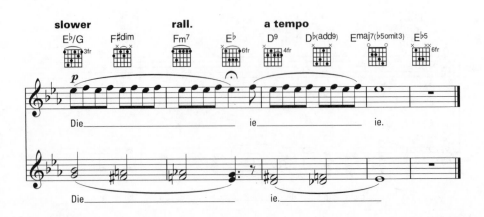

slower   **rall.**   **a tempo**

Die._____ie._____ie.

Die._____ie._____

246

Thoroughly Modern Millie

Words by Sammy Cahn
Music by James Van Heusen

There are those, I sup-pose,_ think we're mad;_ hea-ven knows, the

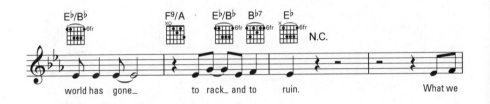

world has gone_ to rack_ and to ruin. What we

think is chic, un - ique and quite a - do - ra - ble_____ they

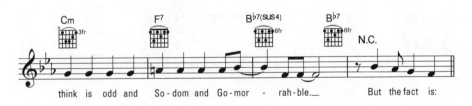

think is odd and So - dom and Go - mor - rah - ble._ But the fact is:

1. Ev - 'ry - thing to - day is tho - rough - ly mo - dern__
2. Ev - 'ry - thing to - day is tho - rough - ly mo - dern__

(check your per - so - na - li - ty), ev - 'ry - thing to -
(bands are get - ting jazz - i - er), ev - 'ry - thing to -

-day makes yes - ter - day slow (bet - ter face re - al - i - ty).
-day is start - ing to go (cars are get - ting snazz - i - er).

It's not in - san - i - ty, say Va - ni - ty
Men say it's cri - mi - nal what wo - men - 'll

Fair; in fact, it's styl - ish to raise your skirts and
do. What they're for - get - ting is this is Nine - teen

bob your hair.___
Twen - ty Two!___

In a rum - ble seat, the world_ is so co - zy____
Have you seen the way they kiss__ in the mo - vies?__

248

if the boy is kiss - a - ble; and that tan - go
Is - n't it de - lec - ta - ble? Paint - ing lips and

dance they would - n't al - low now is quite per - mis - si - ble.
pen - cil lin - ing your brow now is quite res - pec - ta - ble.

Good - bye, good good - y girl, I'm chang-ing and how! So

beat the drums 'cause here comes tho - rough-ly Mo - dern

1.

Mil - lie now!_____

2.

Mil - lie now!_____

N.C.

Till There Was You

Words & Music by Meredith Willson

Original key: Eb major

1. There were bells on a hill,_____ but I
(2.) birds in the sky,_____ but I

nev - er__ heard them ring - ing; no, I
nev - er__ saw them wing - ing; no, I

nev - er heard them at all, 'till there was you.
nev - er saw them at all, 'till there was

2. There were you. Then there was

mu - sic and won-der-ful__ ros - es,__ they__

tell me,— in sweet fra-grant mea-dows of dawn—

and— dew.— 3, 4. There was love all a-round,—

but I nev-er heard it sing-ing, no, I

To Coda ⊕

nev-er heard it at all 'till there was you.

D.C. al Coda   ⊕ **Coda**

Then there was   you.

'Til Tomorrow

Words by Sheldon Harnick
Music by Jerry Bock

Under Pressure

We Will Rock You is a 'jukebox' musical, a form that is freed from the need to connect a dramatic story with songs but is instead required to superimpose a narrative retrospectively onto a song catalogue. The songs of Queen are here linked by a book written by ex-comedian Ben Elton who was aided by Queen band members Brian May and Roger Taylor. The musical premiered in the spring of 2002 at London's Dominion Theatre whose brash marquee, nine years on, remains, ironically enough, one of the few recognisable landmarks in an immediate area that has been largely torn down in a major redevelopment. Most critics loathed the show but audiences loved it. The story proposes a bleak science fiction future where creative thought and individuality are banned and mankind's only hope for salvation is the return of rock 'n' roll. South Africa, Switzerland, Vienna, New Zealand, South Korea, Singapore, Bangkok and Hong Kong. The song 'Under Pressure' has a suitably dystopian feel to it, being an impressionistic 1981 joint composition and recording involving David Bowie and Queen. It came out of jam sessions at Bowie's Swiss recording studio but Bowie himself rarely performed it solo until after Freddie Mercury's death; he did however sing it as a duet with Annie Lennox at the 1992 Freddie Mercury Tribute Concert.

Under Pressure

Words & Music by David Bowie, Freddie Mercury, Roger Taylor, John Deacon & Brian May

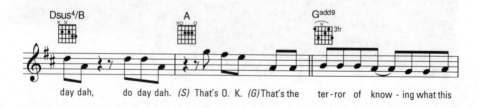

high___ high - er.___ *(S)* Pres-sure on peo - ple, peo-ple on streets.___

(Both) Turned a - way from it all like a blind man,

sat on a fence but it don't work. *(G)* Keep

com-ing up with love but it's so slashed and torn,___ *(S)* why?___

___ Why,___ *(G)* Why?___

___ *(S)* Love, love, love, love. *(G)* In -

edge of___ the night and___ love dares you___ to change our way of car - ing___ a - bout our - selves, this is___ our last chance. This is___ our last dance. *(G)* This is___ our - selves. *(S)* Un - der pres- sure. *(Both)* Un - der pres- sure. *(Piano)* Pres- sure.

What Kind Of Fool Am I?

Words & Music by Leslie Bricusse & Anthony Newley

Original key: D♭ major

♩ = 126

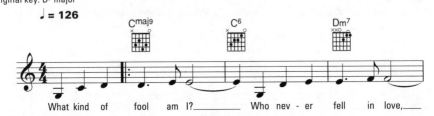

What kind of fool am I?____ Who nev - er fell in love,____

____ it seems that I'm the on - ly one that I have been

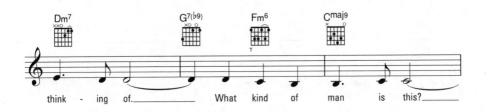

think - ing of.____ What kind of man is this?____

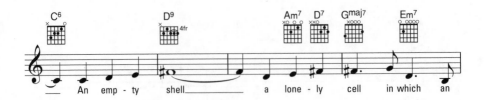

____ An emp - ty shell____ a lone - ly cell in which an

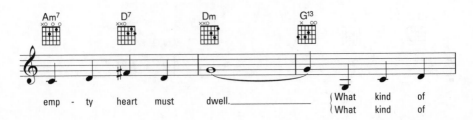

emp - ty heart must dwell.____ {What kind of
{What kind of

lips are these_____ that lied with ev - 'ry kiss?_____
clown am I?_____ What do I know of life?_____

__ That whis - pered emp - ty words of love that left me a -
__ Why can't I cast a - way the mask of play and

- lone like this._____ Why can't I fall in love_____
live my life?_____ Why can't I fall in love_____

__ like a - ny oth - er man_____ } and may - be
__ till I don't give a damn_____ }

1.

then I'll know what kind of fool I am. What kind of

2.

am._____

Written In The Stars

Words by Tim Rice
Music by Elton John

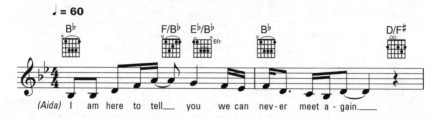

(Aida) I am here to tell__ you we can nev-er meet a-gain.__

Sim-ple real-ly__ is-n't it?__ A word or two and then a

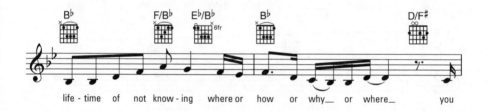

life-time of not know-ing where or how or why__ or where__ you

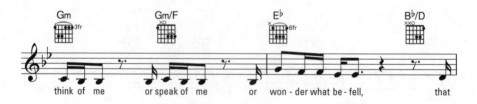

think of me or speak of me or won-der what be-fell, that

some-one you once loved__ so long a-go__ so well.__

(Radames) Nev-er won-der what I'll feel as liv-ing shuf-fles by.

You don't have to ask me and I need not re-ply.

Ev-'ry mo-ment of my life from now un-til I die,

I will think or dream of you and fail to un-der-stand how a

perfect love can be con-found-ed out of hand. Is it

writ-ten in the stars, are we pay-ing for some crime? Is that

all that we are good for, just a stretch of mor-tal time? Or some

God's ex - pe - ri - ment___ in which we have___ no say?___ In

which we're giv - en pa - ra - dise but on - ly___ for a day?___

(Aida) Marry the princess, Radames. *This could be our chance to do*
You can help my people. *something important. Don't you see?*

Noth - ing___ can be al - tered, there is noth - ing to de - cide,

No es - cape, no change of heart, nor an - y place to hide.___

(Radames) You are all I've ev - er want___ but this I am de - nied,___

some - times in my dark - est thoughts___ I wish I'd nev - er learned *(Both)* what it

264

is to be in love,___ and have___ that love_____ re-turned. *(Aida)* Is it

writ-ten in the stars,_ are we pay-ing for some crime?___ Is that

all that we are good for,___ just a stretch of mor-tal time?_ *(Radames)* Or some

(Both) God's ex-pe-ri-ment___ in which we have no say?_ In

which we're giv-en pa-ra-dise but on-ly___ for a day.___

Yakety Yak

Words & Music by Jerry Leiber & Mike Stoller

1. Take out the pap - ers and the

trash,
(2.) room.
(3.) hat,
(4.) looks.

(Sax)

or you don't
Let's see that
and walk your -
Your fa - ther's

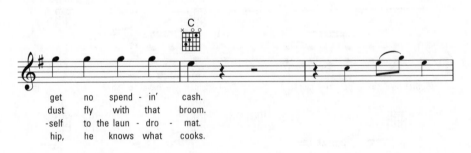

get no spend - in' cash.
dust fly with that broom.
-self to the laun - dro - mat.
hip, he knows what cooks.

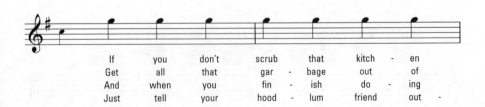

If you don't scrub that kitch - en
Get all that gar - bage out of
And when you fin - ish do - ing
Just tell your hood - lum friend out -

floor,
sight,
that,
- side,

you ain't gon - na
or you don't
bring in the
you ain't got

To Coda ⊕

rock and roll no more. Yak - et - y yak. Don't talk
go out Fri - day night. Yak - et - y yak. Don't talk
dog, and put out the cat. Yak - et - y yak. Don't talk
time to take a ride. Yak - et - y yak. Don't talk

Repeat twice,
then D.S. al Coda

back. 2. Just fin - ish clean - in' up your____
back. 3. You just put on your coat and____
back. 4. Don't you give me no dir - ty____

⊕ *Coda*

back. Yak - et - y yak. Yak - et - y

Repeat to fade

yak. Yak - et - y yak. Yak - et - y

You're The One That I Want

Words & Music by John Farrar

You bet-ter shape up,___ you bet-ter un - der-stand to my heart___ I must be true.___ *(Danny)* Noth-ing left, noth-ing

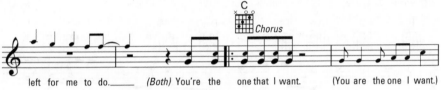

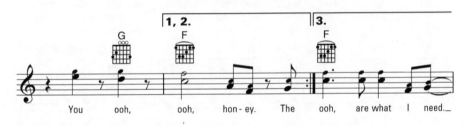

left for me to do.___ *(Both)* You're the one that I want. (You are the one I want.)

1, 2. **3.**

You ooh, ooh, hon - ey. The ooh, are what I need.___

D.S.
D.S.S.
(Repeat Chorus to fade)

Oh yes in - deed.___ *(Sandy)* 2. If you're

Verse 2:
If you're filled with affection
You're too shy to convey
Meditate in my direction
Feel your way
(Danny) I better shape up
'Cause you need a man
(Sandy) Who can keep me satisfied
(Danny) I better shape up if I'm gonna prove
(Sandy) That my faith is justified
(Danny) Are you sure?
(Sandy) Yes, I'm sure down deep inside.

You're Nothing Without Me

Words by David Zippel
Music by Cy Coleman

♩ = 122

(Stine) 1. You are some gum-shoe, you just don't think, well
(Stone) 2. You are so jeal-ous of my track re-cord,
(Stine) 3. You're in my plot,__ I'm still your cre-a-tor,

get this, dumb gum-shoe, you come_ from my ink-well.
Tol-stoy, do tell__ us your fee-ble hack re-cord.
I call each shot,__ I'm your pri-vate dick-ta-tor.

Is your mouth lone-ly with one foot in____ there,
Your weak knees brand_ you soft and un-sta-ble,
(Stone) You are so thick,__ you eat, breathe, sleep fic-tion,

Stone, your brain on-ly holds thoughts I put in____ there.
one small threat and__ you fold like__ a card ta-ble.
I'm your meal tick-et, knee-deep_ in cheap fic-tion.

Just what you are__ I'll spell out,__ you are a nov-el
You drool at my__ ad-ven-tures, your broads in bed are
(Stine) You gloat-ing ig-no-ra-mus,_ you have-n't an-y_

270

271

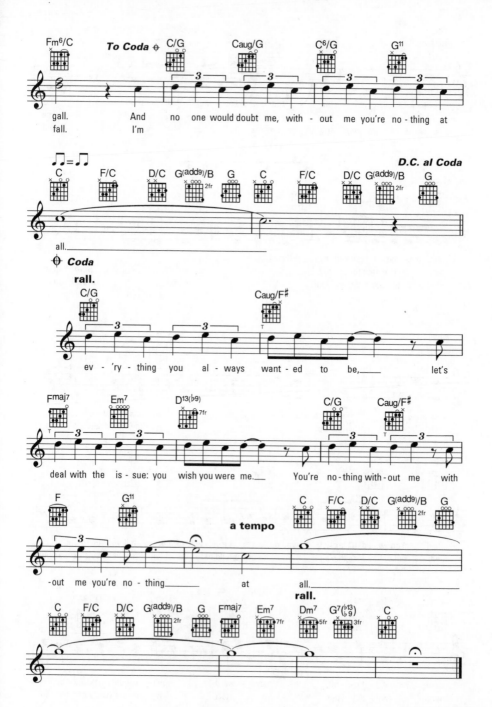